# TIME IN

# TIME IN

## A Handbook for Child and Youth Care Professionals

Author: Michael Burns, C.C.W., B.A.

Editor: Sandra Johnston, B.A., B.Ed., M.Ed.

Illustrator: Pam Ross, H.B.F.A., B.Ed.

**Canadian Cataloguing in Publication Data**

Burns, Michael, 1948–
Time in

Includes bibliographical references.
ISBN 0-9697302-0-9

1. Play therapy. I. Title.
RJ505.P6B87 1993 618.92'89165 C93-091658-1

Second Printing 1999



*Printed and bound in Canada by Hignell Printing Limited*

♾ This book is printed on acid-free paper.

# Contents

# Acknowledgements

This text would never have been completed if not for the diligent editing and abundant emotional support from my partner Sandra Johnston. She has been my inspiration and my companion during this long journey. I would like to thank Gerry Fewster and Thom Garfat for believing in the manuscript, supporting its completion, and promoting its publication. I would also like to thank the *Journal of Child and Youth Care* and the University of Calgary Press, in particular, Denise Szekrenyes and Sharon Boyle. A special thank you to Pam Ross for her talented illustrations and support, to Rhae Ann Bromley for her design of the cover, and to Eileen Eckert for the book design. There have been many typists on this project and I would like to single out Laura Williams for her work on the manuscript. Jerry Beker has been very supportive of my writing since I began and I would like to acknowledge his help in the preparation of the final draft as well as to thank him for his endorsement of the text. Jack Phelan has read through the many drafts of this work and has offered suggestions that have proven to be invaluable. Jack has also been an inspiration to me in my search for excellence in the practice of child and youth care. I would also like to express my appreciation to Henry Maier for his encouragement and advice. Karen VanderVen has been instrumental in this work and I would like to thank her for her enthusiasm and her endorsement of the text.

My greatest appreciation goes to the parents, children, youth, and mentors who have taught me my craft and who have shared a part of their lives with me, to them I will be forever grateful.

The writing of a book is supported and inspired by many individuals to a greater and lesser degree and so, to the many people who have not been named individually, I thank you for your contributions.

Finally, I would like to dedicate this book to my two children, Dan and Sara, who have been a constant source of joy throughout my adult life.

# Preface

Let's hear it for Michael Burns! At a time when so many professionals and parents are scrambling to control kids through the tedious technologies of the day—including "time out"—Michael invites us to look at the possibilities of spending "time in." Such sweet heresy was seldom more needed, or more timely.

But this elegant little manual is no simple exhortation for us to change our ways. Nor is it another cookbook of prescriptive rituals to be blindly followed by those who seek to rise above their vulnerability by becoming "professional." *Time In* calls as much upon the humanness of the practitioner as it does upon the innate potentials of each child to discover and express the self. In this, it provides the most effective of all learning contexts—one that promotes the reciprocal growth and creativity of all participants. How simple and profound.

As co-editor of the *Journal of Child and Youth Care* for the past eleven years, I have perused a plethora of literature in this field and in this particular work, Michael Burns has set a standard that I have constantly sought and rarely found. I cannot imagine any front-line practitioner who would not benefit from having a copy of *Time In* readily available. It took only one glance at the manuscript for me to set about convincing my fellow editor that we should publish it. And, it took only the cost of postage to obtain his enthusiastic support.

Now we pass this gift over to all who take the time to read and hope that they, in turn, will ensure that as many kids as possible are given the opportunity to share the benefits. In my opinion, *Time In* is what child and youth care is all about. Let's hear it for the "real" child and youth care worker!

Gerry Fewster, Ph.D.
Co-editor, *Journal of Child and Youth Care*

# Introduction

fun is laughter,
excitement, style
letting go
running wild
fun is play and play is fun
individually it varies some
fun is a healthy thing you see
it strengthens hearts
it's trouble free
it can come out of nothing
that's for sure
fun recycles, fun endures
take a daily dose of fun
spread it round to everyone
and if you've forgotten how to play
find a child and take a day
lift your heart up to the sun
mimic her
you'll have fun

The mentoring and nurturing of children from early childhood to young adulthood and beyond, by adults who are in professional positions such as Child and Youth Care Workers, Early Childhood Educators, Elementary and Secondary School Teachers, Recreational Leaders and Coordinators, as well as leaders and volunteers in positions of providing activities and/ or instruction to children and youth, forms the basis of this text. There are no tips for choosing day care centers nor are there instructions for financing a university education. There are no blueprints for behavioral manipulation nor are there theories that explain social deviancy. There are no answers to questions regarding hemispheric functions of the brain nor are there hypotheses included that attempt to explain the diversity in children's capabilities. *Time In* is, rather, a book that provides insight and instruction regarding the facilitation and teaching of children and youth in group settings. It is a book about creative play experiences, experiential learning encounters and cooperative social interaction. *Time In* is an action-oriented book that allows the reader to participate actively in the learning process. It can be used as a vehicle to stimulate human interaction and as an instrument to promote awareness of the self and of the other. It attempts to vitalize adults and children; its purpose is to help them to reclaim the vitality that they were born with. Many children and youth, because of the dysfunctional natures of our education and child care practices, are stripped of their vitality and their joy of living. *Time In* and its facilitation of the play experience can help the child and the adult tap into this source of vitality through its open invitation to the participants to experience life in group interaction. The text has no cultural basis in terms of children and youth. Many of the games and activities are from various cultures and their flexibility allows the leader to adapt them to the group's needs. Children with special needs and challenges can enjoy the diversity and the adaptability of the games and activities and the focus on the adult leader to structure the exercises to suit the group's level of development. The games and experiences throughout the text encourage children and youth to value themselves and each other in the context of creative expression. *Time In* provides the adult leader with an opportunity to learn and to teach healthy group interaction. Its diverse storehouse of games and activities provides experiences for individuals and groups who are at various levels of development and it suggests a wide variety of environments. It offers the student and the experienced child and youth care professional with novel and creative methods in which to facilitate human interaction.

Section A, entitled "Play," begins by familiarizing the reader with play concepts and theories; it highlights the benefits of play and delineates the role of the play facilitator. It describes various play environments and the benefits that each milieu has to provide. It concludes with a framework for assessment of developmental needs which allows group leaders to plan and to sequence programs that will be suitable to appropriate development.

The next section, "Play Facilitation," focuses on the basic skills needed to effectively operate group play experiences. The issue of appropriate leadership and the qualities and behavioral strategies needed in order to guide the group are discussed. The subject of whether the adult leader should take control of the situation or choose to remain inactive is dealt with in this section. The concept of developing leadership abilities for all group members is emphasized as a way of attaining a high level of group participation. Methods to develop rapport and the basic skills for relationship development are highlighted. Readers are provided with opportunities for mentoring their leadership skills in order to encourage more effective leadership and facilitation of group play experiences.

The third section (Section C) of the text discusses activities and is dedicated to children and youth for it is they who will benefit most from this section. A potpourri of over one hundred games and activities are presented in order to provide opportunities for individuals young and old to play and to have fun as a group. This section also offers experiences for the newly formed group or for the fully developed and evolved group. There are structured play experiences for the special needs and convalescing child as well as competitive and non-competitive game experiences. There are also activities which require both individual and shared leadership. This whole section provides the child and youth care professional with a collection of ready-made, tried and tested activities that may be used during organized play times or during transitional or unexpected free time occasions.

*Time In*'s last section, "Developing Expertise," focuses on more advanced levels of group facilitation. Continuous development of skills and expertise is necessary even for the seasoned child and youth care professional in order to effectively present the activities presented in this section. Extensive planning, a high level of expertise, and ongoing supervision is critical to their successful outcomes. Section D introduces the complex and powerful use of games and activities that have the potential to heal and to vitalize. The experienced group play facilitator is provided with opportunities to assist the child or youth with expression of repressed emotions and difficult-to-manage feelings. Emotions that cannot be expressed are often energy consuming and they frequently handicap the child in their ability to experience vitality. Relaxation, guided fantasy, and storytelling are suggested as ways of encouraging the child to safely access emotional and experiential worlds. Art, drama, and music are presented as effective mediums which allow the individual to express emotions, thoughts, and behaviors in order to encourage further mastery of responsible and effective self-expression. This section provides over forty structured play experiences that can be used to assist children and youth to become more self-expressive.

This intensive work is further illustrated in the last chapter with the presentation of four complete programs.The programs consist of six, one-hour sessions, each of them interrelated in such a way as to provide an in-depth look into four specific areas: thoughts, emotions, and behaviors; self esteem; peer relationships; and separation or loss of the family unit. This final section provides the experienced child and youth care professional with opportunities to master complex skills that are highly effective in the treatment of emotional and behavioral difficulties.

*Time In* is organized in such a way as to invite the reader to actively participate in the learning experience. Each teaching chapter begins with a metaphor and contains exercises that invite the reader to experience the topic discussed. These exercises are designed to allow the reader to reflect on personal experiences to make learning more meaningful. Self-awareness is essential to healthy interaction and *Time In* offers over fifty exercises to heighten the reader's awareness in order to encourage personal growth and effectiveness.When these individual experiences are shared in a group or in a classroom setting, the reader is provided with accounts of several human reactions to the issues and to the techniques that are discussed. *Time In* presents a unique opportunity for the reader and the classroom participants to integrate self-awareness and individual experiences into the learning process.

The text has been laid out with wide margins to allow the reader to make personal comments or add instructors' notes. The exercises and activities have pauses in them to cue the leader or reader to stop and allow the listener to reflect. These pauses are depicted by a diamond figure (♦) and are not meant to be for any standard length of time. The reader will decide through experience how long to pause. The exercises in the chapter are meant for the reader but they can also be used in a classroom setting for instructors to use with students or for child and youth care professionals to use with their groups.

Finally, *Time In* was written for front-line child and youth care professionals who desire novel and creative ways to provide exciting and joyful group experiences and who wish to provide a respite from the overly controlled, boring, and depressing environments in which many children and youth find themselves confined. Readers and colleagues, *Time In* is waiting for you and encourages your creative self to explore its pages and to come out and play.

# THE THEORY

# PLAY

CHAPTER ONE

# UNDERSTANDING PLAY

My grandparents lived in a very scenic part of Southern Ontario where apple orchards and grape vineyards stretch across the countryside.They owned a tiny wood frame cottage on the edge of a small town.Their land was twelve acres of meadow, woods, pond and barn. Grandpa was a seer, a gardener and a musician.Grandma was a lover, a painter and a seamstress.The gift they gave to us was their capacity to see the good and the bad in everyone. They taught us to value our dark side and to befriend it. They believed in their grandchildren and they allowed us to grow with as little interference and with as much independence as possible. When we needed nurturing they were there to care for us and when we required disciplining they were also available. Our mentors and at times our rivals, they always encouraged us to believe in what we felt was right.They taught us to live life, not to prepare to live it.

All their grandchildren spent time with them on their farm and some of us spent most of our summers there. Our days were spent swimming in the pond, diving off the old maple tree swing, building tree forts and houses in the wood, laughing at Grandpa's jokes or trying to solve his riddles, riding Old Sam until Mel sent us home, and listening to Grandma tell stories of far-away places.
They presented to us many of life's mysteries and gave us the guidance and the opportunity to experience them on our own. Life with Grandma and Grandpa was an adventure—one as easy as child's play.

**Play is an important survival skill for the human species: to play is not only to learn, but to learn to survive.**
**OTTO WENINGER**

Play can be defined in many ways; each definition captures a part but not all of this unique experience. Groos defined it as preparation for life. Montessori called it child's work. Freud said it was a child's way to maintain equilibrium between the needs of the self and the needs of society. Piaget said it was an act of assimilation, characteristic of the initiative stage. Frobel said it was the basis of development for the whole child. Erickson saw play as spontaneous activity motivated by a desire for fun. Play is many things and defies most of its definitions. There are no words to define it but it appears to be best defined by Erikson: Play is what you do to have fun. Much has been written about the importance of play on child development and if play is the art of having fun, then it is critical to life at all stages of development.

This chapter focuses on play in a simplistic and rudimentary way. It sees play as the expression of the life force. Humans express their aliveness through play and this makes it worthy of examination for the child and youth care professional. Play begins in infancy and continues throughout their entire life span. When children, early in their lives, are encouraged to play, to express their aliveness, they feel accepted and their existences are validated. When children are stopped, discouraged or stifled in their play, they feel rejected and wrong in their expression of self. Children at all stages of development learn through their play. They learn the art of being human in all of its complexities. The more they are encouraged to play and to express themselves through their play, the more they learn about who they are and how it is for them to be in the world. Even though play is a learning experience, only the severely traumatized child has to be taught how to play. Children already know how to play and need very little supervision. They can, however, benefit from loving and healthy adults who can act as facilitators when they request one, or their safety needs require one. An adult can structure the child's environment to make learning opportunities more fruitful. Play facilitators can also conduct games or activity experiences which require more structure in a way that is the least intrusive to the child's play experience.

Games and structured activities are a form of play but are less of an expression of the self and more of an expression of self within the confines of rules. Conduct and roles are more clearly defined and play more formalized. Games are generally introduced later in the child's development because of the demands that rules make on the younger child or on the child who is developmentally slow. Games require impulse control, tolerance to frustration, acceptance of limits, and a high level of interpersonal interaction. Children who have not attained these abilities are much happier and better served developmentally when they are allowed less structured play experiences. When the children have reached middle childhood, they are ready for the structure of games. Play for the child in middle or late childhood is almost always associated with rules and organization of thought and behavior. Children in later childhood and teenage years thoroughly enjoy games of all complexities.

The play of early childhood seems to develop in stages, beginning with solitary play where the young child plays alone and does not include others in play. The solitary stage progresses to parallel play where the child plays along side of other children but does not interact with peers by involving them in the play experience. The next stage is associative play where the child includes others in play but there is no effort made to organize or cooperate with these others. The final stage is cooperative play, which involves organized activities and games (Parten, 1932).

Games can be divided into three types: games of physical skill, strategy, and chance (Sutton-Smith, 1971). Games of physical skill are determined by the players' abilities in gross motor activities. The outcome is decided by who has the highest level of motor ability. Games of strategy are determined by the players' cognitive abilities. The outcome is decided by the player or team who has the highest level of cognitive ability. Games of chance are determined by luck. The outcome has no bearing on the players' abilities in the cognitive or physical areas.

Cooperative games and activities of self discovery and self-expression, e.g., therapeutic games, the arts and guided fantasy, usually played by children of middle childhood ages and older, are an interesting bridge between play and traditional win/lose games. The cooperative game has elements of physical skill, cognitive ability, and luck or chance. As well, it adds an emphasis on cooperation and a de-emphasis on competition. This allows more freedom of self-expression which allies cooperative games with play experiences. Activities of self-discovery and self-expression, in the same way, add structure to the child's ability to express the self. Games and activities of this nature have both the elements of play and games.

## Benefits of Play, Games, and Activities

Play enhances social development by allowing the child to practise various social skills in an imaginary context as a rehearsal for social life. Games allow the child and youth to exercise these skills in a more structured and more stressful situation as further preparation for the complexities of social living. Activities can directly prepare the child to deal with social situations. For example, children can role play situations in order to gain insight into their behaviors and the behavior of others. Social development is encouraged through play, games, and activities as the players interact with one another.

Play benefits emotional development through its interactive quality and its expressive nature. Players must both control and express emotions appropriately in order to be understood. This encourages children to befriend their emotions and to learn more about how they operate. Games require more control of emotion but at the same time allow children a vehicle through which to express their feelings. Activities can be structured so that children and youth can directly experience emotion and can openly discuss its effect on them. Emotional development is fostered in play, game, and activity experiences by allowing the child and youth to express emotions and have them identified and discussed.

Cognitive or intellectual development occurs during play as the child experiences and manipulates the environment. Play materials such as sand, water, and blocks provide the child with excellent learning experiences. Density, mass, volume, cause and effect, mathematics, the use of levers, structures, and force are all experienced in the free play situations of the preschool child. Games require the child to use the intellect to strategize, to problem solve, to generate new and creative ideas, to think abstractly, and to enhance language development. Activities can directly challenge the child's cognitive abilities by focusing on specific intellectual tasks, e.g., math games or problem-solving exercises. Intellectual development can be enhanced through play, game, and activity experiences by providing the child and youth with a context in which to explore, exercise, and express intelligence.

Play, games, and activities can also be therapeutic in nature. Play therapy pioneered by Virginia Axline (1947) is a free play experience where the child acts out fears, anxieties and negative experiences through play. A trained therapist watches and records the child's play to gain insight into the child's problems. Therapists and counsellors often use play, games, and activities as a way of building rapport with the child or youth. As well, they encourage self-expression which might not take place in a formal setting but often happens in the context of fun. Fun, in itself, is therapeutic as it brings pleasure and positive feelings to its participants. Games and activities can increase the child or youth's feelings of self-worth. Through mastery of the demands of games and activities, the players feel a sense of accomplishment and pride in their abilities. Activities in the arts provide opportunities for self-expression and self-disclosure which in turn benefit the child and youth. Play, games, and activities are therapeutic tools that provide the child and youth care professional with a variety of opportunities to enhance the lives of the players.

## The Role of Play Facilitator

This book is about play facilitation and how the child and youth care professional can enhance play, games, and activities. It points out specific areas of concentration for the student and the seasoned professional in an effort to mark out the importance of achieving excellence in this role. Child-and-youth-centered play, games, and activities are the focal point of truly successful play facilitation. Much can be learned from the child-centered play approach made popular by professionals in the field of early childhood development.

Children and youth show an insatiable desire for knowledge and understanding in all areas of their development. This paragraph will merely outline the basic concepts of the role of the play facilitator as this concept of play facilitation will be expanded upon in many of the chapters to follow. The traditional role of teacher is a model of one-way communication. The teacher taught and the children learned. The role of the professional or teacher in child-centered learning is a model of two-way communication. The child or youth expresses an interest, a desire, a question and the teacher provides encouragement, motivation, and resources so that the individual or group might satisfy that curiosity, fulfill that desire, or answer that question. The child or youth is able to express an interest in a particular area and the play facilitator is capable of providing access to the necessary resources that are at an appropriate level for the individual or group. The facilitator can provide assistance and encouragement in order to motivate the child or youth to obtain sufficient material and experience which, in turn, will help them to answer their own questions and to fulfill their own desires. With this type of approach the adult and child relationship is more equal and the child or youth has control of the experience as well as the power to manipulate the environment in order to suit individual needs.

The child is encouraged to explore areas of interest, and these high interest areas dictate the direction in which the play facilitator is to lead. Child-and-youth-centered play offers an experience or experiences for the players that are suited to their levels of development and provides opportunities for optimal learning and pleasure.

By using the child as the focal point in play facilitation and the environment and activity as the instrument, the child and youth care professional offers an experience that is truly child-centered. Play facilitation in more structured environments and activities will be the emphasis of this text; however, the successful play facilitator must have a child-centered focus.

> **When children are free to come to terms with materials, when they can explore under the guidance of their own curiosity and not in ways directed by the teacher, they will handle their materials in a wide variety of ways which are truly creative.**
>
> **ALICE YARDLEY**

## Bibliography for UNDERSTANDING PLAY

Axline, V. (1947). *Play therapy*. Boston: Houghton, Mifflin.

Barnett, L. (1990). Developmental benefits of play for children. *Journal of Leisure Research, 22*, 138–151.

Elkind, D. (1987). *The hurried child*. Toronto: Addison-Wesley.

Noren-Bjorn, E. (1982). *The impossible playground*. New York: Leisure Press.

Parten, M. (1932). Social play among preschool children. *Journal of Abnormal and Social Psychology, 27*, 243–269.

Sutton-Smith, B. (1971). Play, games, and controls. In J.P. Scott (Ed.), *Social control* (pp. 361–370). Chicago: University of Chicago Press.

Weninger, O. (1992). *Playing to learn: The young child, the teacher and the classroom*. Springfield, IL: Charles C. Thomas.

Yardley, A. (1988). *Senses and sensitivity*. London: Rubicon Publishing.

CHAPTER TWO

# PLAY ENVIRONMENTS

Melinda's gardens were always a favorite attraction for the kids in our town.Wherever you walked on Melinda's property, either inside or outside, you were always experiencing nature. In one morning visit you could hear twelve different song birds, sight deer and hawks with their young, pick armloads of vegetables and fruit,gather a magnificent bouquet of flowers, and enjoy breakfast under the skylight in the kitchen with any one of a number of animals.

Melinda's house was like a flower shop with a whole array of blooming plants no matter what time of year. The three main rooms each had a different temperature, level of humidity, and amount of light to suit the different types of plants. Melinda was so relaxed and self-assured that you could easily enjoy yourself in all her environments. She answered our questions and allowed us to explore the many different areas. Melinda was not secretive and hid nothing from us. Her gardens were open to the people in our town and many of them visited regularly. Her gardens were a big part of my growing up.

**A playground should be like a small scale replica of the world, with as many as possible of the sensory experiences to be found in the world included in it.**
**RICHARD PATTNER**

The first consideration, for the child and youth care professional who wishes to conduct successful and stimulating play activities, is the enviroment in which the game or activity will take place. Play takes place both indoors and outdoors and this chapter will explore both possibilities as well as a combination of the two. Milieu often dictates the success or the failure of an activity. Play environments influence whether the children or youth will join in the play experience with wonder or whether they will play with some reservations or even whether they will play at all. Children and youth require play and recreational areas to be physically and emotionally safe, as well as to be stimulating and diversive. An environment that provides structure with opportunity for free expression is the ideal. Play environments need to be versatile in order to provide a variety of possibilities for a wider spectrum of experience. Simplicity of design and utility of available equipment make play environments into warehouses for the creative experience.

Children are drawn to the outdoor play areas, playgrounds, open fields, and wooded places in their environment. They come alive in the presence of nature, and they identify with it. Nature has a way of returning a child or youth to a state of homeostasis, to a state of balance or equilibrium. The quiet, withdrawn child suddenly becomes noisy and adventurous when building a fort in the woods. The aggressive and overactive child softens and quiets as s/he cares for a pet rabbit. When child and youth care professionals include the outdoors as part of their planning and presenting of activities, they find that their success increases significantly. Educators who include environmental learning as part of their curriculum have seen the dynamic role that the outdoors can play in the learning process. Environmentalists understand that part of the task of saving the environment is centered on the education of coming generations. When children enter the forest, their whole psychology and physiology change to accommodate to this different world. Playgrounds, wood lots, backyards, alleys or streets; the outdoors do make it all come alive.

When you cannot be outside there is lots of fun and excitement to be had inside. What the outdoors does for the quality of the experience, the indoors makes up for in predictability and dependability. A comfortable indoor place, spacious enough to accommodate the group, provides a reliable and consistent space in which to play. The indoors is also much easier to control and to manipulate. The temperature can be controlled, privacy can be maintained, safety is often more easily assured, and overall control of the group is much simpler. Furniture and equipment can be added, moved or removed, in order to give the indoor environment versatility. The ideal combination of both indoor and outdoor activities gives the child and youth care professional an environment suitable to any and all of the activities in this text.

## The Environment

Indoors or outdoors, the surface, the parameters, and the equipment are also necessary considerations in the choice of play environments. Certain surfaces like wood, tile, concrete, sand, grass, clay, or pavement affect the quality of the activity. Boundaries or parameters insure structure and control of the activity. Walls, fences, hedges, hash marks, or painted boundary lines allow for the necessary structure to ensure the success of the activity. Equipment, from furniture to plastic hoops, add versatility and variety to most activities. Comfort, versatility, and aesthetic value are the primary considerations in considering a space.

Proper and responsible attention to physical safety can prevent most, if not all, accidents with children and youth. An activity played on a sandy surface could be disastrous when played on a paved surface. An outdoor hike or canoe trip without proper training and experience can be a potential tragedy. Faulty and poorly maintained equipment can result in serious injury. Lack of attention to possible toxic or harmful aspects of the environment can also have negative consequences. The child and youth care professional should always be conscious of potential safety hazards or safety issues and should control the environment in order to maintain a high level of safety for the group experience. Emotional safety is also crucial; however, this is a more complex issue which will be discussed in other parts of this book.

Children's outdoor activities can be enhanced by providing the right kind of experiences for them through the careful planning and manipulation of the play environment. Children's knowledge and understanding of plant and wildlife in their natural habitat can be enriched through careful planning of the hiking and camping experiences. A wide variety of games and activities can be provided outdoors.

The first introduction to the outdoors for most children takes place in their own backyard. It could be a part of the five hundred acre farm or, it could be a small balcony in a major city; yet, wherever it exists, most children begin to learn about nature in their own backyards. Children who live in large metropolitan areas may not have a space of their own outdoors but, often, they have access to a neighbourhood playground. The backyard, for toddlers and preschoolers, can be the ideal place to enhance the child's learning experience. The child and youth care professional can be instrumental in providing outdoor learning experiences for children in their own backyards. The first step in providing these experiences is to assess the play space according to space, layout, surface, and equipment.

The amount of space for most families is limited and, often, the backyard or front yard space is a multi-purpose area. The major questions to be answered here are: How much of the backyard is available for children? Does the space have boundaries; for example, fences and hedges? Are there out-of-bounds areas? Are there any safety hazards to be aware of? Does anyone else require the use of the space? The answers to these questions provide the necessary data in order to assess the space available.

The best way to determine the layout is to make a map of the backyard. This map should include all aspects of the yard, such as the location of any trees, shrubs, storage areas, play equipment, gardens, etc. When mapping out the yard, try to include the measurements of these areas. This map should provide an overview of the area. When considering the layout of the yard, be aware of how the traffic flow in each area affects the whole space; determine the direction of flow; and consider possible ways of improving the efficient use of the areas available by redirecting the traffic flow.

Grass, sand, humus, wood, cement, gravel, wood chips, asphalt, and outdoor carpeting provide unique play experiences for the child. Assessment of the potential types of playing surfaces available to the child in the planning of backyard play experience allows for the efficient use of play space, as well as for a diversity in play experiences.

Swing sets, garden plots, bicycles, wagons, badminton nets, footballs, hoses, beams, building equipment, sand boxes, pools, trees for climbing, and a host of other equipment enhances the play experience. Make a complete assessment of play equipment by listing what is available and what is needed.

Once the physical plan is drawn up and an assessment is made, determine the uses of the backyard in terms of the developmental levels of the individuals using the area. These developmental levels determine how the backyard will be used. The younger the child, the more quickly these levels change; this requires long-term considerations of the child's developmental play requirements.

Children's play needs are physical, social, and cognitive in origin, and these three needs determine the construction of backyard play spaces. The area of physical play is concerned with large muscle activity; running, jumping, climbing, crawling, skipping, kicking, and throwing are a few activities that allow the child to develop in the physical area. Social play varies from being alone to having interaction with others; or, it can be role playing alone, or in interaction with others. This social area helps the child learn to understand the socialization process experientially. Cognitive play involves problem solving, observational learning, the manipulation of objects, making choices, and interpreting outcomes. Play equipment and activities can provide the child with opportunities to develop cognitive skills.

The indoor environment for the child is also important for it is here that a large part of the day is spent. Indoor environments need to be stimulating and activity oriented. Like outdoor environments, space, layout, surface, and equipment are necessary considerations.

The space considerations for indoors are similar to outside. Children function best in a space that has enough area for large muscle activity and a quiet space that is away from the more active areas. The indoor environment can make good use of shelves, containers and hangers to make a more easily organized play area.

The layout of the indoor space should insure a functional flow of traffic to each area and ideally the different areas should be accessed individually. Sometimes furniture can be positioned to set up boundaries to assist in creating useful play areas.

The surface of the indoor space is important in planning play environments. It dictates whether water or sand can be used, whether the child can lie down on the surface, and the possible hazards for activity.

Board games, balls, hoops, and so on enhance the indoor environment by making it more activity oriented. Large pillows, puppet theatres, art easels, toys, and punching bags enhance play opportunities and provide opportunities for creative expression.

Children's developmental needs should always be considered when planning indoor play environments.

## Exercise 2:1

- Draw a map or floor plan of the environment in which your group activities are held.
- Colour in the areas that are out of bounds to all children, i.e., for staff only.
- With another colour, shade in the areas that are admissible to children only.
- With another colour, shade in the areas that are readily available to both staff and children.

- For child and youth care professionals in residential settings: are there individual or personal areas where only the individual (child/adult) is able to probe, e.g., a locker, desk drawer, or closet that is out of bounds to everyone except the individual?
- Examine your map or floor plan, and comment on the areas shaded.
- Is there an imbalance in the environment?
- Would it be useful to have areas for children only?
- Is there a need for a private space for each individual?
- Does your environment make good use of the equipment and resources available?
- Is there easy access to all play areas?
- Are there distinct boundaries?
- Are there any safety or health hazards?
- Now draw an ideal map or floor plan of the existing play environment.
- Discuss your floor plan improvements.

## Playgrounds

Adventure playgrounds became very popular in Europe; they were filled with junk, staffed by adult play supervisors, and the children were allowed to use fire, earth, and water in order to create their own play worlds. Adventure playgrounds have proven to be highly popular and have an excellent safety record for children (Greenman, 1988). They exist in many metro areas across Canada and the United States; however, their popularity with adults does not compare to their European counterparts and, thus, their numbers are very low. Child and youth care professionals, concerned parents, and local officials can easily provide similar types of experiences for children by using their existing facilities, and by making alterations that would make them more playful. Trips to nearby nature trails, animal farms, wildlife areas, and outdoor events can supplement the play experiences of the neighborhood play group. The first step to providing optimum play experiences for children outdoors is to take stock of what is needed, and what is readily available.

Children's outdoor play needs are amazingly simple; they can create their own play worlds out of nothing except their imaginations and their abilities to socialize. This concept should be kept foremost in the minds of child care professionals as they plan outdoor play spaces. There is a point where enchantment and disenchantment converge in adults' attempts to enhance play experiences. Elaborate equipment and over-supervision of play experiences make work out of child's play. Children get frustrated, and adults feel unappreciated when good intentions turn sour. Whenever possible, the children who are using the play space should be involved in its planning, building, and maintenance. This allows for children to feel a responsible part of their play area, and encourages them to express their wants and needs in order to make the play space more useful.

Children develop their large and small muscle skills through experiences in running, jumping, swinging, climbing, sliding, rolling, kicking, throwing, hitting, bounding, balancing, riding, chopping, digging, and pounding. Open spaces and pathways on different surfaces provide children with opportunities to meet their running needs. They can run fast, slow, start and stop, chase, and be chased. Children love to run, and out of their running comes skipping, jumping, tiptoeing, and other forms of locomotion. Hammocks, ropes, vine swings, nets, and conventional swing sets give children opportunities to swing alone or with others. A variety of swinging experiences enable children of all ages to meet their needs, and to challenge their abilities. Platforms, trees, logs, poles, hills, tires, nets, stairs, and stumps provide a variety of climbing and leaping experiences for children at all levels of physical development. The risk and challenge provided by the climbing and leaping experiences is especially attractive to them. A hill in a playground can be a place to roll; it can be a snow slide in the winter, and a water slide in the summer. A metal slide can be built into the side of a hill to provide sliding experiences for children at all levels of development. Walls, nets, bats, hoops, barrels, targets, grass, and pavement provide opportunities for children to throw, kick, hit, and bounce balls, frisbees, bean bags, snowballs, and hoops. Balance beams, ropes, platforms, logs, nets, and bicycles allow children to test and to challenge their abilities to balance themselves. Earth has an essential part in play experiences; sand and mud provide large muscle experiences such as pounding, chopping, digging, and hoeing.

Adventure, challenge, and risk are very much an integral part of children's overall development. In addition to having a place for activity, children also need a place for quiet, rest, and less active play. A well-treed area, a shelter with tables, a tree fort, a cabin, a playhouse, a tent, a patio, or wooden boxes all provide places for quiet reflection and less active play. Socialization and dramatic play often happen at quieter times in these places. Children find privacy and solace in their "cubicles" whatever they might be; tunnels and large sewer pipes provide interesting places to hide and to play in. Playground equipment that has moveable and changeable parts gives children freedom to change their environment and allows them to be more flexible in their play than permanent structures do; for example, wooden boxes, canvas, and rope provide the potential for a wider variety of structures than a permanent lean-to does.

Children need to create as well as to destroy; they need to build and to take apart; they thrive on experiences that require them to use their imaginations and cognitive skills in order to interact with their play environment. Fire, earth, and water coupled with basic building tools and supplies give children such an opportunity. Fire fascinates children for many reasons; it has power and destructive capabilities; it provides energy and warmth; and it has the ability to create and to destroy. Children in early childhood and middle childhood often are not given the opportunities to experience fire because of its extreme danger. When activities and experiences are well supervised and developmentally appropriate, children can experience this awesome element. A candle, a gas stove, a small contained fire, a large bonfire all carry this fascination. The building and the use of fire should always be well supervised; children should be well instructed in identification of fire, fire hazards, prevention, first aid, and fire safety.

Earth carries an equal fascination. Earth extinguishes fire; it is an element in the creation of plant life; and it, too, is powerful and is part of the life cycle. These properties can best be seen in the garden plot, flower bed, stand of trees, nature trail, meadow, or forest area. The child can also create structures with the earth: sand castles, mud pies, hills, mountains, ditches, and coves are all possibilities. Digging tools and sand areas make the experience easier for younger children. Earth, like fire, provides a primary learning medium.

Water, the element that not only extinguishes fire, also can move the earth and make it change. Children's fascination with water exists because of its power and its ability to create and to destroy. It, too, is primary in its ability to teach and to give exposure to many of the child's developmental needs. Water and earth provide ditches, ponds, oceans, and lakes, as well as that much coveted substance—mud. Water also gives life to the plants in the garden, the lawn, the flower beds, as well as to the wild flowers and weeds in the ditches. Water can be frozen outside in the winter for skating and sliding and, in the summer, it can be used for cooling, for quenching thirst, and it can be sprayed on plastic for a water slide. Children can be taught basic mathematics, physics, and science through witnessing water change in size, shape, and density. When the elements of fire, earth, and water are available for children, they continually find ways to interact with and to experiment with their basic properties.

Basic building tools such as a hammer, nails, saw, drill, or screws and screwdrivers add a whole different dimension to children's play experiences. Lumber of all different sizes, wooden boxes, sawhorses, and planks provide children with opportunities to create a living and playing environment that is constantly changing as the imagination dictates. Buildings and boats, freight cars, and automobiles grow out of the interaction of children with these materials.

When children are allowed to interact with the animal and vegetable worlds as part of their play experiences, their learning experiences are once again increased, and their humanity, as well as their position in the life cycle, can be realized. The act of digging up a small section of the playground and planting vegetables seems like a small task; yet, it carries with it a myriad of learning experiences. The entire life cycle of nature takes place in this special environment. Seeds are germinated into plants that grow from seedlings to adult plants and on to maturity; these plants produce seeds to complete the cycle and die in the process. When children take an active part in this process by preparing the soil, planting the seeds, watering and weeding the small plants, nourishing them to maturity, and harvesting them, they experience their life in harmony with their environment. Many lessons and experiences can be provided by a small garden plot.

Animals, too, can be part of the play experience. Wild animals, birds, reptiles, fish, and insects often visit the playground areas. Feeding stations can be set up to encourage their presence; bushes, plant life, ponds, and shelters can be included in order to further attract them to the playground. Children can learn about the local wild animals, and about their habits, by observing them firsthand. Some play areas have cages and shelters that allow children to view these animals and other domestic animals at a closer range. Environmentalists and naturalists can be consulted and utilized in the effective care of these animals, as well as be encouraged to participate in the learning experiences of the children. The process of caring for plants and animals, as part of the playground experience, makes the area even more special and exciting for the children and adults. Wooded areas and marshes also provide excellent varieties of plant and wildlife; playground groups can visit nearby areas that provide this experience.

Finally, children require places to wash and to use the toilet. Some play areas come equipped with cooking and eating areas for children. A place to keep out of the rain and wind is also a useful addition to play areas when the weather becomes severe.

Most of the needs identified above can be met with only a few additions to most conventional play areas. When discarded lumber materials, wooden crates, a canvas, a rope, a hill, or a wall on a piece of tarmac are creatively utilized, checked for safety, and adult supervised, children can create play environments that will enhance their development and their life experiences.

## Exercise 2:2

- Make a plan of your neighborhood playground.
- Assess it according to the section on children's needs in outdoor play experiences.
- Redesign the area, and pay particular attention to safety, traffic flow, and the maximum use of space.
- Draw a plan of the proposed changes.
- List possible funding sources to pay for changes.
- Call a meeting of neighborhood children and parents in order to propose ideas that will encourage them to enhance the play experiences of their neighborhood.

## Nature Walks and Day Hikes

The use of off-site areas for games and activities add variety and excitement to the experience. Hiking is an excellent way to enhance environmental awareness.

The first rule of hiking is to come prepared for any weather, and this involves clothing, primarily. The first consideration is footwear. Nature walks, in most cases, require running shoes and socks; for longer hikes and backpacking trips, hiking boots with two pairs of socks are preferred. When on long walks, children can be encouraged to carry an extra pair of socks. Clothing should always depend upon the climate of the region, and most climates fluctuate somewhat. When hiking, one should be prepared for wet weather and for cold weather. It is always possible that ponchos and sweaters will not be worn, but they are a comfort when needed. Each child can carry a small pack with necessary gear and snacks inside. Hiking in marshlands obviously requires boots, and these can be packed as well. Headgear is a must for most hikers, sheltering them from the sun, the wind, and the rain. A pair of woollen mittens can come in handy for the cold days. Children should be given an appropriate clothing list in order to ensure that they are prepared; this also prevents them bringing too much gear.

The second rule of hiking is to know exactly where you are going, and to tell someone in authority where you will be. The best rule for the person who is organizing the hike is to be familiar with the trail beforehand. This allows for better planning on hike day so that the children will benefit best from the activity.

The third rule of hiking is to carry a first-aid kit and to bring someone who is trained in first aid. Anything can happen on even the most well-planned hike, and when you are prepared for safety, there will be no catastrophes.

The fourth rule of hiking is to leave the environment intact. The cutting down of tree limbs and trees is inexcusable. Wild flowers and plants should be observed, drawn or photographed, and not picked or trodden upon. All refuse should be taken back and disposed of, including that left by others. Collecting of insect and plant specimens to be studied at a later date should be kept to a minimum. Bird nesting areas, wildlife dens and burrows should not be damaged or handled. Children can be taught at an early age to understand and to preserve our natural environment.

Good preparation makes for a good hike. Goals can be set by the child care professional and by the children planning the outing in order to give it more direction. Experts in wildlife and nature can be brought along to point out some of nature's mysteries to the children.

Play environments have a critical role in normal child and youth development. Play and recreation areas can depress or stimulate activity, encourage or discourage creativity, limit or increase socialization, stifle or encourage self-expression, and can unite or divide the group. Careful consideration and manipulation of the play environment is a primary factor in terms of group satisfaction of the play activity.

> **Environmental playgrounds, which encourage an active interaction with plants and animals, water and dirt, weather and the life cycle, offer children education at its most compelling.**
>
> **JIM GREENMAN**

## Bibliography for PLAY ENVIRONMENTS

Darst, P.W. (1980). *Outdoor adventure activities for school and recreation programs*. Minneapolis, MN: Burgess Publishing.

Dattner, R. (1969). *Design for play*. Cambridge, MA: M.I.T. Press.

Fletcher, C. (1976). *The new complete walker*. New York: Alfred A. Knopf.

Friedberg, M. (1975). *Handcrafted playgrounds*. New York: Vintage Books/ Random House.

Green, M. (1977). *A sigh of relief.* Toronto: Bantam Books.

Greenman, J. (1988). *Caring spaces and learning places.* Redmond, WA: Exchange Press.

Mason, J. (1982). *The environment of play.* West Point, NY: Leisure Press.

Moore, G., Cohen, U., & McGinty, T. (1978). *Case studies of child play areas and child support facilities.* Madison, WI: University of Wisconsin Press.

Nonen-Bjkorn, E. (1982). *The impossible playground.* West Point, NY: Leisure Press.

Pattner, R. (1969). *Design for play.* Cambridge, MA: MIT Press.

## CHAPTER 3

# PROGRAM DESIGN

The third little pig realized that an appreciation of safety in his new environment would be essential to his happiness. He decided that building a house which would satisfy those needs would be his next course of action. His "little voice" told him that, from past experiences, there was a "right time" for everything. Sensing this, he set out to formulate a location, a design, and a building plan for his new home. He sat down under a sturdy oak tree, situated on a stream in a quiet meadow and began his plan. He built and rebuilt his domicile by forming pictures in his mind and by daydreaming about how it should look. He talked to others who had experience in building and consulted writings on the matter. The pig considered angles, mass, and materials; he checked his ideas with how he felt about them, for verification and clarification. After some time, he said to himself, "This is it—my best idea—a house of stone, positioned close to the trees and on top of that hill!"

He sat back and smiled. His plan of action was now clear, and all that was left before construction was to put his plan down on paper. Off he went with pencil, paper, and a strange-looking ruler, humming a very familiar tune.

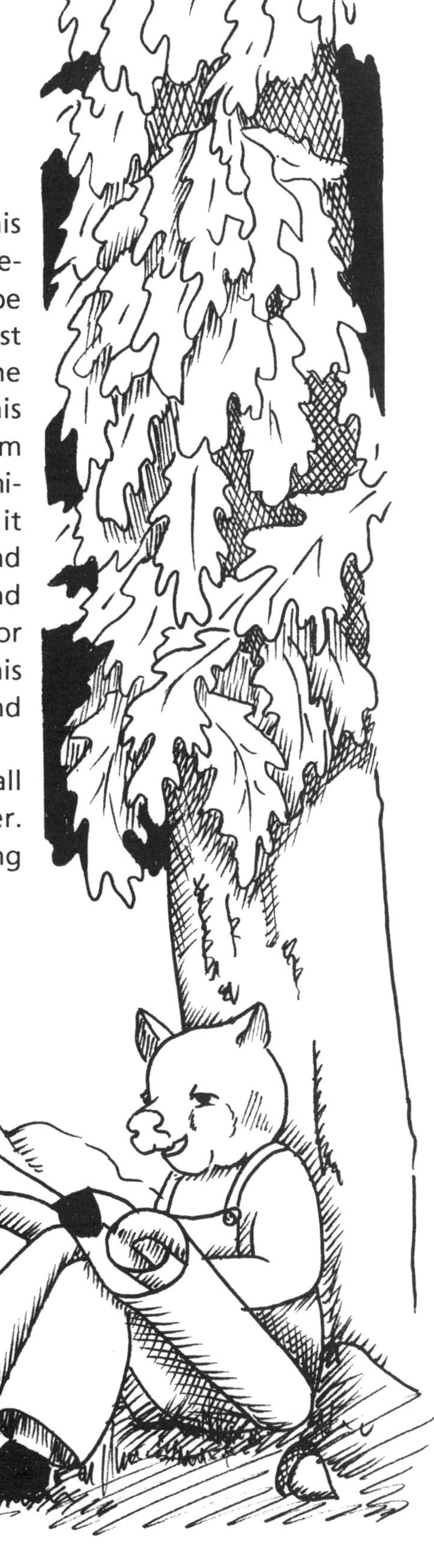

**The function to planning is to institute and give direction to action.**

**Gerard Egan**

Program design is the careful planning, organizing, and sequencing of group activities for the purpose of insuring a positive and productive group experience. The process considers the developmental needs of each child in the group, as well as the needs of the group as a whole. It addresses the sequencing of activities within the time framework of the program in order to maximize its benefits. It explores the elements of structure and spontaneity in the programming of activities and it points out the need for goal setting and program evaluation in successful program designs. The result of the third little pig's plan and process was a house that withstood the tests of time and the power of the wolf.

## Programming for Developmental Needs

The social, emotional, intellectual, spiritual, and physical development of children is the basis of child and youth care. Children's play activities can enhance this development. When designing children's play activities, their developmental levels and the developmental expectations of the activity are of primary importance. This requires a knowledge of the normal and atypical growth and developmental stages of the specific children within the target group as well as a knowledge of the developmental expectations of each activity presented in the program.

Programs designed in response to the developmental levels of the group members are highly successful and, often, require little behavioral intervention. The following is an outline to be used as a guide for anticipating the developmental levels of children in different classifications, and it suggests types of activities that will work best. These profiles are not extensive, and the reader who is not familiar with child growth and developmental levels is advised to read any one of the reference books on child development used in the writing of this chapter.

### Early Childhood

Group activities, highly structured activities, and activities that require accomplished motor skills are not functional for the age group from four to six years. Children at this age function best when they are in programs where different activity centers are set up for them, and where they are allowed to explore these various play centers. Art, dramatic play, music, sand, water, blocks, and large muscle centers provide children in this age group with the variety necessary to meet their varied developmental play needs. This variety in developmental levels, and the high incidence of developmental lags in this age group may make cooperative activities and team games inappropriate. The game concept, which includes following rules, winning and losing, is not recommended for this age group. This group typically has a short attention span; and so, play experiences need to reflect this. Children in this age group often find it difficult when confronted with several choices, and may require adult intervention in order to assist them in this area. They are usually eager to learn and, therefore, highly motivated to try new activities, provided that they can easily succeed and that they can receive immediate feedback for their efforts. Children in this age group are highly imaginative; this makes art and drama excellent avenues for expression. They love storytime, finger plays, and silly songs, provided that they are presented to them for short intervals that correspond to their attention spans. At times, these children can be antisocial or they may indulge in parallel play; or, they may play cooperatively in small groups. Their abilities can vary from day to day. Repetition and routine allow this age group to practice their developmental strategies and tasks, which assists them in learning their boundaries and capabilities. Children at this age are developing their eye/hand coordination and they may not have established dominance in terms of right or left handedness. Their fine and gross motor abilities need to be exercised and challenged; therefore, activities that provide these types of opportunities are the most useful. In general, play activities should be center based, as well as varied and reflective of a group of children who have a wide variance in abilities and interests.

## Middle Childhood

Children in this age grouping are seven to nine years of age. They are slowly increasing their attention spans, developing and mastering large and small muscle skills, and broadening their abilities to socialize and to cooperate. Programs that encourage further development in these areas are essential to the success of games and activities for the middle child. Developmental levels of children in this age grouping are still quite diverse; therefore, the open-ended, free-flowing types of programs used for children in early childhood are also very successful. The middle child needs help defining his/her limits because often s/he overestimates his/her abilities. Cooperative and well-structured activities can assist these areas of development by providing the limits through the structure of the activity. The cooperative element allows the child to make a better assessment of his/her abilities by comparing him/herself to others in a non-competitive milieu. The middle child has a tendency to demand too much of him/herself and s/he can be quite impatient, impulsive, and sensitive to failure. Non-competitive games and the use of small groups of peers in each activity provide an experience that gives each individual child enough exposure to the skills required of the activity. This limits the numbers who witness the child's failure and impatience, and provides a structure that promotes patience, cooperation, and success. The middle child has a need to be both an active and a passive participant in play. Small groupings allow the adult leader to give individual attention to the child who needs to withdraw as well as to the child who wishes to master the skill.

At their best, middle children are active and energetic. They enjoy tests of strength, endurance, and being challenged. Through running, climbing, skipping, jumping, the middle child experiences bursts of energy and often tires easily. The trampoline, large and small balls, ropes, ladders, climbing and balancing equipment, water play, tag, and wrestling allow the child to burn off these bursts of energy in an appropriate and self-developing way. Children in this age group are better equipped cognitively and emotionally to appreciate quiet games and activities. At the more mature end of middle childhood, children can attempt and be successful in team activities. Competition can also be introduced but it should not be a focal point in overall programming.

At this age, the peer group is increasing in importance, and the dividing line between males and females is clearly drawn. Sometimes even antagonistic towards each other, boys and girls often do not want to be paired up with a member of the other sex. This sense of we-ness can be capitalized upon by giving children a part in developing programs and learning/teaching new games.

## Late Childhood

Children in late childhood, from ages ten through to twelve, are generally more flexible, more predictable, and more accepting than any other age group is. This is an age range where children are very peer oriented; often, they form little cliques and speak in coded language. They are developing a strong sense of individuality; they are concerned with personal performance and with perfecting skills. As a result, they can often be moody, self-conscious, and argumentative. They have a healthy sense of fair play and honesty which makes organized team sports and activities highly desirable at these ages. They are assertive, curious, accepting, and adventuresome. Activity programming for this age group works well in large and small groups. They have the self-esteem, the power to concentrate, and the physical ability to play almost any game or activity. Most children in this age group are sociable and friendly, and if behavior becomes a problem, the group usually knows how to deal with it.

### Early Adolescence

This age group is from twelve to fifteen years of age. The importance of the peer group has been heightened by adolescence. They are loyal to group principles and tend to be egocentric when comparing themselves to the out group. Cliques are strong, and rebellion towards adults and authority intensifies in this age group. Programming for adolescents must include the group members in at least fifty percent of the decision making. Creative problem-solving techniques, group discussions, and efficient use of group resources will assist this age group in developing their own activities, special events, and rules of conduct. The child and youth care professional can play a role as a resource person, as a facilitator, and as someone able to assist in the efficient operation of the program. All group members should be encouraged to take an active role in programming. Physically and emotionally, it is a time of constant change for adolescent individuals. Growth spurts, hormone changes, and the emotional stress brought on by puberty are reflected in their somewhat unpredictable behavior. The marginal feelings of no longer being a child, but not yet an adult, can cause frustration and confusion for this age group. Females mature faster than their male counterparts and this can cause some difficulties in relationships. Social gatherings, parties, outings, and group projects are highly valued activities by this age group. Team sports and a wide variety of recreational activities occupy their leisure time. Games with risk, or simulated risk, allow this age group to satisfy their sense of adventure, to use their newly-developed skills in abstract thought, and to exercise their problem-solving skills. The early adolescent is venturing out and exercising independence and autonomy. The child and youth care professional will benefit from lowering tolerance levels for independent behaviors and by tempering the need to control. The adult leader can withdraw somewhat from this age group by supervising the children through this developmental stage and by maintaining a positive influence through facilitation.

### Late Adolescence

This age group, fifteen to nineteen years of age, is seeking adult status yet abilities to achieve this vary with each individual. They are extremely loyal to their peer group and need that group's approval in order to feel a sense of belonging. This can be a very tumultuous time within the family. The adolescent is trying to break away from parental ties, and is developing new bonds outside of the family. This individuation causes the adolescent to become more self-reflective and to make attempts at becoming self-sufficient. Appearance is important, sex is important, and ideals are important. Discussion groups concerning these topics and others suggested by the group can serve as ways for teens to learn about and to explore safely and, with guidance, areas that are critical to their well-being.

This group loves team games and a wide variety of sport activities. They enjoy most of the games and activities used in the other age groups. The child and youth care professional can expect full involvement, planning, and execution of programming from the adolescent. They can take total responsibility for most of their games, activities, and special outings. The role of the adult is to facilitate the group experience, and to assist in the efficient operation of the program.

### Atypical Development

Children of every age, for various reasons, have delays and disturbances in their growth and development to adulthood. Some children are so seriously delayed or damaged emotionally that they have much difficulty functioning in a program. Children with physical, emotional, social, or intellectual delays require more planning and expertise than would otherwise be required. Child and youth care professionals often deal with entire groups of children with exceptional needs and, in turn, must produce exceptional programs in order to be successful. Many, if not all, children with exceptional needs have met with failure and ridicule from children as well as from adults in many different settings. Their resistance to becoming involved in group activities that challenge their abilities is an obstacle to group satisfaction. Problems with attention span, frustration tolerance, impulse control, self image, relationships, withdrawal, aggression, communication, and physical and mental ability are major considerations in program planning for children with developmental delays. Careful planning, expertise, and realistic expectations are needed to make activities and experiences enjoyable and productive.

## Sequencing of Activities

The timing and ordering of activities is of prime importance to program design. When the right activity is presented at the right time, the possibility for success and maximum benefit is greatly increased. This right time for the group is determined by the group's developmental level and by the pace of the program. The pace of the group, in most cases, is an abstract determination made by the group leader on the basis of the leader's particular knowledge and experience with this particular group as well as on the social-emotional and environmental influences in place at the time of the activity. This is where the group leader's ability to be flexible helps to adjust the activity levels to suit the pace of the group; for example, Jack, the group leader, observes that his normally quiet, docile group of nine year olds has had three incidents of aggressive outbursts in the first half hour. Some group members have become inactive and are functioning more as onlookers than participants. Jack calls a time-out and asks the group to form a circle. After verbalizing his observations, the feedback from the group is that the new supply teacher is really mean. Five minutes of discussion and ventilation and a shift to more introspective, less competitive activities involving dyads and small groups (chosen by Jack) provide the group with a worthwhile and meaningful hour of enjoyable experiences. Jack is able to salvage a doomed program and to turn it into a learning experience by calling time-out and by relying on his backup programs which he always keeps stored in his memory for times like these.

The group leader must be able to anticipate shifts in the group pace, just as Jack did in the above example, and also, to respond to the change of pace. The analyzing of the group's developmental stage and social-emotional pace is best done in the opening portion of the program. The pace of the group can often be anticipated by investigating what experience or experiences the group or its individuals have had just prior to the program. For example, the pace of a group just arriving after a long bus ride would be quite different from a group just being dismissed from recess or a gym class. The emotional level of a group that has just returned from a movie is quite different from one returning from a weekly home visit.

The adult group leader who anticipates the pace and activity level of his/her group is more apt to program activities that meet the needs of the group as they arrive and to lead them to the desired level of performance and enjoyment. Alternate plans provide the flexibility to the program that allows for changes in mood, weather, group composition, and for any unforeseen developments requiring a change in programming. The program design must be flexible enough to meet the here-and-now needs of the group. The most creative and best-organized plan is doomed to failure unless it has alternatives to support it. The child care professional must be prepared at all times to go with the flow of the group and to change any and all activities if the group situation warrants it.

A useful way of sequencing a program is to divide it up into three basic parts: a beginning, a middle, and an end. The beginning, sometimes called the introduction or warm-up, is intended to ease the transition from the state of non-groupness to a state of groupness. It is a time when themes and concepts can be introduced to the group. This initial part of the program can also be the time for the adult group leader to assess the group's mood and pace. The beginning activities should be a way of preparing the group for the middle or the body of the program. When the warm-up has achieved its aim, the body of the program can begin. The middle or body of the program is the activity, or series of activities, that give meaning and purpose to the group's getting together. The body of the program is structured in such a way that it allows the free flow of activities to reach their respective goals, while maintaining a level of comfort and enjoyment for the group members. The adult group leader must structure this time in order to be sure to leave enough time for the cool-down. The ending or cool-down of the program provides closure to the body of the program, and prepares the group for the transition of leave-taking. This may mean slowing down the pace, consolidating lessons or themes, and generally leaving the group with a sense of completion. The seeds of new ideas, directions, or concepts can be planted at this time in order to give the group something to ponder until they meet again. Programs structured this way can provide optimum group experiences for its members.

## Competition in Children's Groups

The use of rivalry in team sports and in individual competitions is a well-known technique that can motivate and unite individuals in order for them to attain new levels of excellence. Competition does have its place in children's activities; however, its use raises concerns among educators and lay people alike. In the past two decades there has been an ever-increasing shift towards non-competitive and cooperative games in activity programming. Non-competitive games are considered to be less stressful and to promote self-confidence in the child. Competition can be successful in children's groups; however, certain procedures need to be followed and certain questions need to be asked:

Do all members feel comfortable with one another? Can group members make mistakes and still feel capable? Does the activity allow all members to compete at an average or basic level? If the activity allows for a handicap or advantage to be given to certain players, is it presented to and dealt with by the group appropriately?

How is the competition to be presented to the group? Is it reflective of an attitude that fosters good sportsmanship and clean fair play? Does it promote respect for both teammate and opposing player?

Are proficiency and increased ability recognized as primary goals in the activity? Are rewards primarily non-materialistic and viewed as secondary to the activity?

Are activities presented in graduating degrees of competitiveness in order to allow monitoring of group reactions?

Do the group members have fun and take pleasure in the activity?

There has been an over-emphasis on competition in children's activities for a very long time in our society. Competition is a useful element in some group activities; and, kept in the proper perspective, it builds character and self-esteem for all children involved. If it is used extensively, especially in social recreational activities, it runs the risk of instilling hostility, poor sportsmanship, added pressure on the child to perform, as well as other adverse effects on the individual group member's self-esteem. Child and youth care professionals must be ever cognizant of what effect added competition will have on group dynamics.

Non-competitive activities provide opportunities for children to enjoy the pleasure of skill attainment in an atmosphere of support and cooperation. They are structured in such a way that they enable children at various levels of developmental functioning to interact in a social play environment. Cooperative games teach socialization and goal attainment through interactions based on mutual respect and collaboration. There are no winners or losers, just participants; the enjoyment of interaction becomes the primary focus. The absense of competition reduces the threat of damage to self-esteem. Conflict is also minimized which lessens the incidence of behavior problems among group members. Non-competitive, cooperative games are excellent for developing cohesion in a newly formed group: as bridges between activities, as warm-ups and cool-downs for program activities, and as ways to introduce a format for discussion of feelings and attitudes. Their uses and strengths make them a must for all programmers.

## Evaluating Programs

Program evaluation is necessary for effective programming and it can assist the group leader in determining continued programming. The evaluation process tells the leader which activities are successful with what age groups and under what circumstances. Evaluation presents the child and youth care professional with the opportunity to grow and to advance skills as a programmer and as a facilitator by using this feedback in order to strengthen the program.

The group members, the group leader, as well as an outside professional, are in an ideal position to evaluate program activities and the total program itself. The group members can give valuable information concerning the enjoyment and satisfaction quotient of the activity to be used. They can also generate creative ideas to be used to enhance both of these factors. The group leader can add personal observations and conclusions concerning group performance and adjustment to the activity. The group leader can give feedback on the amount of preparation and level of difficulty the activity demands, and can also provide creative solutions and short cuts in order to refurbish failing programs. Outside professionals can be most useful as observers and resource people for the group leader. They can provide ideas, suggestions, and criticisms to the group leader in order to augment the functioning and the desirability of the activity. The outside professional may take part in or observe the group, from time to time acting as a seer and as a recorder of the group's level of functioning and how it responds to the group leader.

Program evaluation must look at the developmental needs of each child or youth and must reflect the intent of the original program design. Programs are presented to the group in order to achieve a specific purpose. This purpose can be defined by a goal or series of goals that outline what it is the group wishes to accomplish. These goals can be broken down further into ways in which the goals will be reached and these ways are called objectives. The purpose, the goals, and the objectives can form the basis of the evaluation process by measuring whether they have been accomplished.

A rudimentary evaluation process would require the group leader to determine the purpose or purposes the group has been formed to accomplish. For example, the purpose of the group might be to provide early adolescent males with proper guidance in the practice of safe sex. The leader's next procedure would be to state goals for the group so that the members might have the opportunity to achieve their purpose. Using the same example, the group goals might be: to provide a safe atmosphere for the group members to speak openly and honestly about the various topics; to present the material for discussion in a orderly and properly sequenced manner; to provide the most recent data and information on the topic; and to present the information at an age-appropriate level to provide for optimum learning and informed discussion.

The final step for the group leader would be to list a series of objectives for each goal so each level of progress or lack of progress can be determined. A list of objectives for the first goal in the example might be: speak with personnel in order to procure a quiet and comfortable room for the group meetings; arrange the meeting room furniture to provide an atmosphere of equality; form a set of standards and safety precautions that would insure confidentiality; and discuss with group members at the first meeting any issues they may have with regards to group safety. The purpose, goals, and objectives can be shared with the supervisor or consultant as well as the group members in order to insure that they are appropriate for the group. Once the purpose, goals, and objectives have been established, the degree in which they have been accomplished can be measured. When the program is in progress, evaluation can insure that the group is centered on its purpose. When the program is completed, the data can be gathered from all three sources and utilized to improve the program delivery.

Evaluation, both ongoing and at completion, can provide child and youth care professionals with the necessary information to upgrade their skill as group leaders and continually enhance the productivity of the group.

> **We are continually faced by great opportunities brilliantly disguised as insoluble problems.**
>
> **ANDREW MATTHEWS**

## Bibliography for PROGRAM DESIGN

Egan, G. (1986). *The skilled helper: A systematic approach to effective helping.* Pacific Grove, CA: Brooks/Cole Publishing.

Matthews, A. (1988). *Being happy.* Los Angeles: Price Stern Sloan.

Orlick, T. (1982). *The second cooperative sports and games book.* New York: Pantheon Books.

Pearce, J. (1985). *Magical child matures.* Toronto: Bantam Books.

Santrock, J., & Yussen, S. (1984). *Children and adolescents.* Dubuque, IA: Wm. C. Brown.

# PLAY FACILITATION

CHAPTER FOUR

# THE GROUP

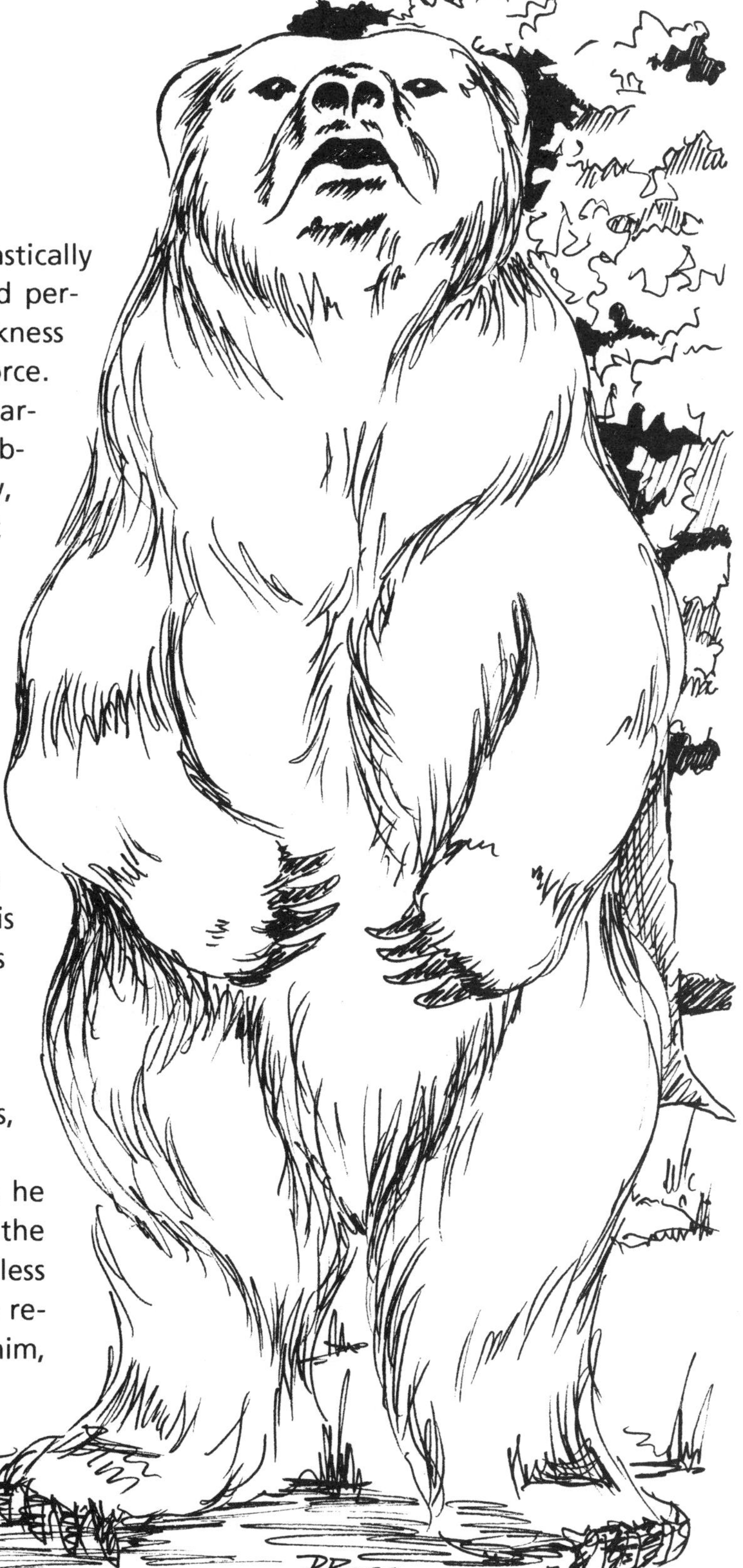


The life of the forest was changing drastically and all its elements were worried and perplexed by the meaning of this change. A sickness was weakening and killing the very life force. Plants, animals, and minerals were disappearing, leaving only deposits of a lifeless substance; the forest was disappearing. This day, a great assembly has gathered in the forest and many have spoken and listened to the problems they commonly face. A bear known to many as Kamo arises to speak.

"On behalf of Nature!" his eyes, blood-red from many sleepless nights, looked intently at his audience as he began to speak, "There is harmony in the forest when nature is allowed to prevail: there is purpose, there is cooperation, there is a healthy balance. The way of Nature is one of reliance; plant, animal, and minerals all act and react in relationship. We must help one another to regain what we have lost and communicate so we can adapt to each other's changes. Change, my friends, appears to be our only poem."

The bear sat down, having said what he had travelled so far to say. The union of the forest was in danger and he feared that unless others were to agree to give as well as to receive, that he, and the generations after him, would be filled with the sickness.

**It is within groups that competencies, attitudes and values are formed.**

**DAVID & FRANK JOHNSON**

Group dynamics, the nature of group life, is the study of groups of individuals in process: how they relate to each other, how they function as a unit, and how they react to their environment. The study of the complexity of life in the group requires a cognitive separation of it into parts without losing the gestalt of the experience. Each group is different with its own heart and soul. This chapter will point out specific areas, various dynamics, and predictable group behaviors. It asks the reader to take note that groups are dynamic. Life in the group, like life in the forest, is one of interdependence and change.

In order to be an effective facilitator of group experiences with children, a basic understanding of group dynamics is most useful. A knowledge of how groups form, and why groups develop, can assist the adult leader in effective group management. Insight into what behaviors are healthy and normal for groups can assist the leader in encouraging and/or discouraging certain behaviors and attitudes. An awareness of the forces that impact on group performance make it easier for a group facilitator to provide a healthy and safe milieu. An understanding of group roles, and of how to encourage positive leading, provides the adult leader with strategies for encouraging healthy role development. The group leader, with an understanding of group dynamics, can more effectively guide the group towards its maximum potential.

Children are required to function in a wide variety of group situations that vary in complexity and importance. The demands and requirements placed upon a child, as a member of a family, are very different from those placed upon him/her as a member of a swim team. The importance of belonging and of feeling accepted in a peer group is much different than the child's relationship to the larger society. If children are given a safe environment in which to explore as many types of relationships as they feel necessary and, if they are taught the values of group cooperation, they will be exposed to all of the skills that are necessary to live a socially healthy life.

## The Importance of Group Work with Children

We are born in relationship, we develop in relationship, and we realize our self-worth in relationship. The world is becoming populated at an alarming rate. Our cities and towns are growing and with expansion, confederation and cooperation with one another is becoming more and more important. The very survival of the planet and its species is dependent upon how well we cooperate in dyads, triads, small groups, large groups, communities, countries, and as people of the world. The skills necessary to accomplish the kind of harmony and coefficiency are most easily taught to our young people as they grow and develop. We, as leaders of groups, must also model cooperation and compassion in order for these lessons to be integrated into action.

When children are taught to satisfy their personal needs in conjunction with the needs of the group, they are able to learn a skill that will benefit their immediate worlds, and this will set a precedence for their expectations of the larger environment. Cooperation and consideration of the group will once again become a focus of healthy living. We must change to this if we wish to develop into and survive in partnership with the rest of the world.

Group experiences for children and youth can be facilitated in such a way as to nurture and to reward the types of skills and attitudes important to healthy group and community living.

## Healthy Group Interaction

Healthy groups are a balance of three main aspects: task, maintenance, and dynamics.

The aspect of task refers to the goals and expectations of the group. The reason for the group's existence is usually reflected in its task aspects. Jean Clarke in her book, *Who Me Lead A Group?*, divides groups into four types according to their task (Clarke, 1984).

A discovery or awareness group is formed to raise its group members' awareness around a specific issue or topic. The emphasis of this group is usually on personal aspects of the group's individuals. Group members get together to learn in a shared relationship. A group of children who are studying science or ways to clean up the environment would be considered discovery groups.

A support group is formed so that individual group members can exchange feelings, hopes, and concerns around a specific topic or problem. The emphasis of this group is for each member to share and to identify the commonality of their experiences. For example, a group of children who are diabetic may form a support group to help each other deal with the problems and concerns that they share.

A skill-building group is formed so that the group members might learn or improve upon a specific ability. The emphasis of this group is often upon the group leader who has mastered a specific talent. A group of children learning C.P.R. is an example of a skill-building group.

A planning group is formed for the purpose of future action. A planning group often gathers in order to make recommendations or to prescribe a set of procedures in order to achieve a specific goal. A group formed to plan the Valentine Day Dance would be considered a planning group.

Each of these four types of groups all have a specific goal, objective, or desired outcome which becomes their task or reason for existence.

## ♦ Exercise 4:1

- Find a relaxing position and allow your thoughts to drift to the different groups you were involved with when you were in grade school, or in high school, or more recently. Allow your thoughts to pass freely from group to group. Give yourself fifteen minutes to recall these groups from the past.
- Now write down three to five groups that you found the most pleasurable and three to five groups you found the least pleasurable.
- Analyze as to why they were or were not pleasurable. From this analysis you will derive more information as to why some groups were more enjoyable than others.

The maintenance aspects of a group concern the emotionality of the members and of the group as a whole. The reason for the group's success or failure largely has to do with how well the group members are maintained emotionally. Do the group members feel satisfied and eager to participate in the group's task? Do they feel a sense of trust and safety within the group proportionate to the demands of the task? The maintenance aspects of the group can be identified in terms of three different areas: inclusion, control, and affection.

The individual group member must feel included in the group and needed by the group in order to be a productive and satisfied group member. Inclusion is vital to the group's ability to grow to its potential. The children within the group are at various stages of emotional development. Most of the issues in these stages involve the feeling of belonging and of being a part of their world.

The issue of control, on the other hand, is also a prime consideration for the group member. The healthy participation in the group activities requires the power and control of the activity to be shared among its members. The activity, game, or exercise that the group is participating in requires that the status and power of group individuals are fairly and evenly distributed. The question the child asks is "What is my status and power in this group?"

The emotions and the level of trust among group members are the major factors when considering the maintenance of the group. The affection aspect of the group defines how well the individual will feel about performing the group's task. When emotions are considered important and worthy of consideration, children are able to respond with emotionally healthy behaviors which insure satisfaction among group members.

## ♦ Exercise 4:2

- ♦ Take out the list that you made in exercise 4:1. There is a good chance that the groups you listed as the most pleasurable were the ones where the maintenance aspects of the group were considered.
- ♦ Relax yourself once again and conjure up group experiences from the past that you found most enlightening. Allow yourself to think back to group encounters where you learned something valuable about life. Give yourself fifteen to twenty minutes to remember three to five instances.
- ♦ Describe the impact these situations had on you and list the emotions and physical sensations you experienced.
- ♦ Read your list to yourself or to a friend and recall the aspects of the groups that you were in, e.g., what was the task; how important or unimportant were the maintenance aspects of the group?

The dynamic quality of a healthy group allows it to grow, to change, and to develop as the challenges of the task and maintenance aspects evolve. Groups where creativity is valued, where power and control is shared, and where open communication is taught and respected, grow and develop towards their potential in time. The growth and positive development of the group relies heavily upon its ability to change, to respond to new ideas and challenges, and to openly confront problem situations. The dynamic qualities of the group can be affected primarily through the process and the content of group interaction.

Group process describes the way in which the group communicates. The participation, leadership, power, decision making, problem solving, conflict resolving, and morale of the group are the process elements. When the group interacts and communicates in a dynamic way, more possibilities can be realized through shared process.

The content of the messages, verbal, as well as non-verbal, and the interpretation of the content also reflect the dynamic qualities of the group. When content of communication reflects flexibility and ownership in group process, the individuals feel more connected and thus, more able to risk the pain of a dynamic relationship. Communication needs to be accurate and a feedback system that allows for validation is necessary. The content and meaning of group life is very important to its dynamics.

The ability to be dynamic has a certain risk factor for the group members. Change always means loss and gain. Change also involves moving from a familiar way of responding to a less familiar way and this often results in anxiety or stress until equilibrium can be established. Loss means pain; stress and anxiety means pain. Trust in the group is a major factor in its ability to be dynamic. When the group members trust that they will be able to support each other through the pain of change they will be more amenable to the dynamic forces.

## ♦ Exercise 4:3

- Take out the list that you made in exercise 4:2 of the three to five learning experiences. Sometimes lessons that we learn are painful and involve difficult to manage emotions. Remember the incidences one by one and note any changes in the group that took place just before or shortly after your learning experience.
- Relax yourself and recall the group experiences that you have recalled in both exercises 4:1 and 4:2. Recall those groups and evaluate the level of health. Allow yourself fifteen to twenty minutes to focus your thinking on these group experiences.
- Take out a sheet of paper and draw three columns: one for the task aspects, one for the maintenance aspects, and one for the dynamic aspects. Apply this idea to three group experiences from the past and diagnose and evaluate the task, maintenance, and dynamic aspects of these group experiences.

## Healthy Groups

A healthy group can be defined as a group of individuals who share feelings of belonging and pride as members of a collective. They feel that there is purpose and merit in the combining and coordinating of their collective talents and efforts. Group members communicate openly, value each others' opinions, and feel a sense of trust and safety in the group milieu. They are able to share roles and status in the group. Leadership responsibilities change to match the situation and the expertise of group members. They are able to confront problems and to see them as systemic issues and not as personality issues. There is conflict within the group and conflict resolution skills are part of each member's abilities.

## ♦ Exercise 4:4

- Read over the definition of a healthy group in the last paragraph. Continue to read it until you are able to envision such a group. Remember this group does have weaknesses and problems; it usually begins fairly fragmented.
- Relax yourself and visualize such a group; listen to the dialogue and try to get a feeling of what it must feel like to belong to such a group.
- If you have not done so already, imagine a group of children interacting in this way. Take all the time you need to get a solid representation of this experience. How would you see yourself in this picture as the adult leader/facilitator of this group? What would your behavior be like?

A healthy group has acquired a balance between its task, maintenance, and dynamic aspects. This type of group develops over time and is largely based on the combined past group experiences of each member. When working in children's groups, realistic expectations and well-planned strategies allow the adult group leader to develop such a group but only if the children are capable of such an experience. The model for a healthy group allows the child and youth care professional to set a standard for group interaction.

## Group Rules

The most effective way to set up enforceable rules within a group is to have the members take an active part in deciding on what they ought to be. A good rule of thumb is if you do not need a rule, do not make one. Here are some useful suggestions when the group decides on the rules.

1. When one person talks, the rest of the members agree to listen.
2. Starting time, finishing time, and clean-up times are to be clearly decided upon.
3. Yes/No to eating, drinking, smoking, etc.
4. Personal issues discussed in the group are confidential.
5. All members are to have an equal voice and vote.
6. Decide whether consensus or the majority rule will be the deciding factor in conflict resolution.
7. Decide whether group membership will be limited or open to new members. How does someone become a member? Can anyone lose group status?
8. No physical or emotional harm is allowed.

## How to Develop Healthy Groups

The first step is an obvious one and that is to be a healthy person and to model appropriate behavior consistently. The adult group leader's behavior is constantly being evaluated by the children in the group. The model for positive and healthy relationships for the group members is the adult group leader.

Educate group members and provide opportunities for them to learn appropriate social skills. When children understand what constitutes group health and can appreciate its worthfulness, they will be more capable of working towards this goal. Effective communication skills such as assertive statements, open-ended communication, and active listening can be taught to children through group exercises and games. Problem-solving techniques can also be taught to most children. Preschoolers can understand the basic sharing rule that solves the problem of toy ownership. Children can be taught problem-solving techniques in varying stages of complexity that will give them skills to help them to deal with group problems. Conflict resolution is another important skill that children can learn in the group environment. They can learn to express their feelings, to empathize with others, and to compromise solutions that reflect the group's needs as well as theirs.

## Brainstorming to Resolve Conflict

The most important factor in the creative process of brainstorming is that all suggestions are written down and are not judged until the process is completed. Sometimes in the less conventional, more bizarre solutions, there are truly creative answers. Here are ten simple steps that make up the brainstorming process:

1. Identify the problem.
2. List all possible and impossible solutions.
3. Go over this list and exclude or cross out any solutions that are impractical.
4. Prioritize all the possible solutions.
5. Select the top two solutions.
6. Discuss the solutions in terms of practicalities, money, time, and energy.
7. Decide on the best solution of the two chosen.
8. Make an action plan: Who will do what by when.
9. Set up a time when the solution can be evaluated by the group or a subcommittee.
10. Evaluate the solution and if it is not working, select a new solution and repeat the process.

Facilitate group health by providing activities that require cooperation and promote non-competitive play. When group goals are set by the adult leader and the group members, the task aspects of the group are clearly defined. The group has some ownership in these goals because they participated in their creation. The adult group leader can facilitate the use of skills such as conflict resolution, effective communication, and problem solving by directing the group to use their skills at appropriate times when the group is together. Games and activities that require leadership to be shared among the group members help to promote the dynamic qualities of the group. Games that do not eliminate members or that count them "out" can help to build group trust and to lower the level of competition. When the adult group leaders provide a safe environment for the members, one that does not tolerate emotional abuse, children find it easier to trust and to risk being authentic. When new groups are being formed, games and activities should provide opportunities for children to get to know each other in dyad, triad, and small groups before being asked to play as a large group. Games that involve trust should not be introduced until members know each other, until they are able to communicate effectively, and until status is reasonably equal. The facilitation of appropriate and effective activities to promote group health require careful planning on the part of the child care professional.

Evaluation of group goals and objectives allows the group to stay focused on the task elements of their health. Evaluation of the group's morale, the group's atmosphere, and the group's level of participation in the task elements, allows the group leader to diagnose where the group is developmentally and where it needs to focus its energies in order to become healthier. An evaluation of the leadership skills of the adult group leader is also necessary in order for the group to be happy, healthy, and efficient. All group programs should include an evaluation process that gives direct feedback to the adult group leader and to group members.

### ♦ Exercise 4:5

- List the groups you belong to now, i.e., family, classroom, teams, etc, in a column along one side of the page.
- Beside each group write down what you believe your role in that group is, e.g., leader, clown, initiator, spokesman, etc.
- Beside each role listed, write descriptive adjectives that most reflect how you act out this role; e.g., quiet leader, boisterous clown, etc.
- Throughout the week, share your list with the members of each group and get their reactions as to how they see you in the group.

## Roles

The final consideration in this chapter for effective group management is the awareness of the types of roles played by group members. An understanding of these roles, and their effect on the dynamics of the group, is a useful piece of knowledge for the child and youth care professional. Various professionals from different disciplines working with groups have identified a number of roles played by group members. These roles, too numerous to mention, are present in one form or another in most groups. In this chapter, we will concentrate on the roles of the clown, the scapegoat, the newcomer, the loner, and the aggressor/dominator.

The clown, joker, wise guy, wit, distractor, or whatever the label chosen to describe this group role, is the person in the group who can make others laugh. This ability, in and of itself, can be one of the greatest assets in the group. When the clown's behavior is appropriate and the style of humour is healthy, the role provides a safety valve for all group members. Anxious or embarrassing situations, when handled with humour, can be dealt with in such a way that individuals can save face. Laughter is a contagious and a healthy activity for all group members. When the clown's role is overplayed, however, it can be counterproductive to the group's health. It can slow down or even halt the progress of group tasks. The clown's need to make others laugh, can be used by group members to fulfill their need to avoid uncomfortable situations by allowing the joker to distract them.

Individuals, finding themselves stuck in the role of the clown, may often resent always having to be cheerful. They may suffer when the group becomes more comfortable with each other and the need to relieve tension is not as great. Healthy clowning needs to be encouraged and to be fostered in all group members. Unhealthy clowning needs to be discussed, confronted, and shifted to a more productive means of interaction.

The scapegoat, doormat, or gopher is someone functioning in a very unhealthy role. These characters will do anything to receive approval which includes admitting to acts they did not commit, setting themselves up to be ridiculed by others, as well as engaging in other self-destructive behavior. This character can carry the negatives in the group, and thus, allow others to escape their consequences. This role can be shared by more than one member of the group, and it can be a very difficult role for the novice child and youth care professional to deal with. The adult leader will have to work extra hard in order to develop solid relationships with the group leaders and key members involved in the scapegoating. It is wise to maintain a non-judgemental attitude when dealing with this problem in order to model appropriate behavior; however, the child and youth care professional must have sufficient control of the situation in order to ensure group safety. If there is to be a confrontation, emphases must be on violation of the rule, rather than on violation of another human being. A high degree of respect for human dignity must be maintained at all times, and this tactic of confronting or arguing about a rule, rather than denigrating a human being, gives the child an opportunity to sustain his dignity. In most instances, once a solid rapport is established, this method of confrontation when dealing with scapegoating is very effective.

The newcomer to a group situation, especially if the other group members have developed relationships with one another, is an outsider to the group and is trying to gain acceptance. This situation can be very stressful until this person feels accepted by the group. Entering into a new group can sometimes be very difficult. The child and youth care professional needs to develop quick rapport with a child who finds him/herself in this role in order to help the transition from outsider to insider. These children sometimes take on a negative role if they feel they will not be accepted for who they are. Sometimes they agree to stay on the outside of the group and function as loners. Some children handle this transition well, and others, both members of the established group and newcomers, need to work very hard at accepting their role and reaching out to others in order to rise above this situation. The loner is a familiar role to most children, and it can be both satisfying and painful. Every man, woman, and child needs to have a certain portion of the day to be alone with their thoughts. Some children, especially those who have very little time alone, may choose one of their group experiences as a time to be alone. More often, children who have had difficulty in the past socializing in peer groups, will tend to place themselves apart from the group. A child with low self-esteem may not feel that s/he is worthy of acceptance into the group. Much like the newcomer, the loner is functioning outside, or on the periphery of the group. The child and youth care professional, as a play facilitator, can build a relationship with the loner and ease that person into other relationships by means of group games and activities. The implications of group work for individuals from middle childhood and beyond are far reaching and each child and youth care professional needs to be in constant contact with these vast and varied inferences. Close supervision and proper evaluation of skill level in the process of group work with children and youth are necessary to optimally benefit each group member. The proper management of group behaviour and insight into group dynamics is the main focus of this section on play facilitation.

> **Norms of a group are constructed both from expectations of the members of their group and from the explicit and implicit directions of the leader and more influential members.**
>
> **IRVING YOLAM**

## Bibliography for THE GROUP


Botermans, J., Burett, T., VanDelft, P., & Van Splunteren, C. (1987). *The world of games: Their origins and history, how to play them and how to make them.* New York: Facts on File.

Corey, M., & Corey, G. (1977). *Groups: Process and practice.* Pacific Grove, CA: Brooks/Cole.

Clarke, J. (1984). *Who me lead a group?* San Francisco: Harper and Row.

Deacove, J. (1974). *Games manual of non-competitive games.* Perth, ON: Family Positives.

*The NESA activities handbook for native and multicultural classrooms.* (1984). Vancouver, BC: Native Education Services.

Johnson, D., & Johnson, F. (1987). *Joining together: Group theory and group skills.* Englewood Cliffs, NJ: Prentice-Hall.

Yolam, I. (1985). *The theory and practice of group psychotherapy.* New York: Basic Books.

CHAPTER FIVE

# LEADERSHIP

Constance, a very awkward adolescent, wanted desperately to become a juggler. She could feel this need grow in her as each circus, carnival, and minstrel show passed through her town. The sight of the hoops and pins masterfully manipulated to suit the performer's fancy cast a spell over her. What a spectacle! The crowd would cheer and whistle and Constance could see that they were mesmerized by the jugglers' display of magic. So Constance began to juggle with two tennis balls. Slowly, she began to feel and to listen to the experience; to watch and to concentrate on each small detail; and then she began to relax. Slowly, the objects and the person began to form the singular experience of juggling. While she was practising, Constance would remember those impressive jugglers from her past and, with each memory, her confidence and abilities grew. She increased her dexterity through imagery and rote. More and more hoops, balls, and pins were added to her repertoire. Her performances became more elaborate and her audiences grew larger and larger. One day, she found herself in the center ring and the audience was spellbound as the juggler performed her magic.

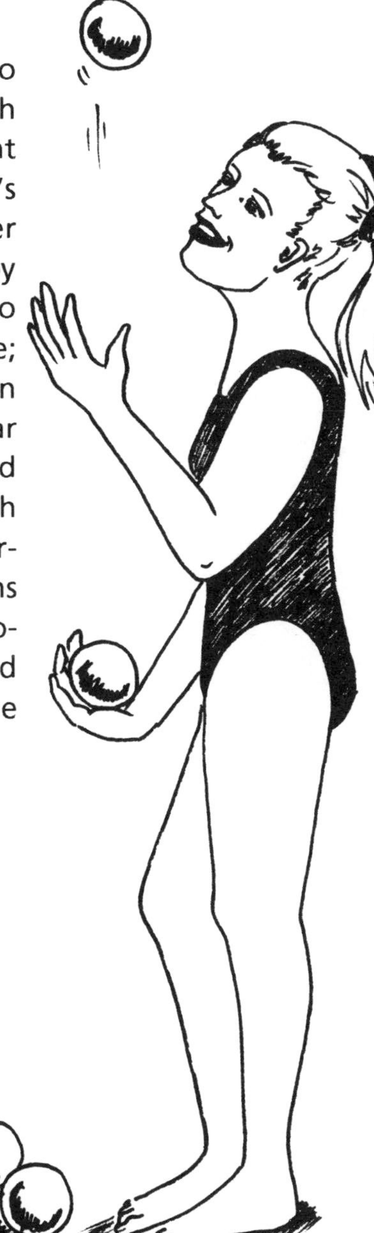

**The seeds of great discoveries are constantly floating around, but they only take root in the minds well-prepared to receive them.**

**JOSEPH HENRY**

Effective leadership is a lot like juggling because it requires a coordination of a number of abilities and traits. This collaboration must mesh with the manipulation of a group of individuals sometimes travelling in opposite directions. The child and youth care professional will need to study and to practise all the necessary skills, to develop the proper attitudes and like that awkward teenage juggler, become an accomplished professional. This chapter will focus on leadership development, styles of leading, the qualities necessary for effective leadership, and strategies useful in developing leadership abilities in children and youth.

Skilled leaders play an important role in the overall development of children and youth. Their influence allows children to grow and to develop physically, emotionally, socially, intellectually, and spiritually.

Physically, through organized games and activities, the adult group leader promotes the use of both large and small muscles. The skilled leader models the need and importance of regular exercise and encourages appropriate physical exercise and contact among peers.

Through the supervision of activities that encourage healthy expression of feelings, the adult leader creates an opportunity for emotional expression. Modeling the importance of empathy while handling the feelings of others provides direction for the child or youth. Emotional development is further enhanced through the provision of opportunities for children and youth to become familiar with all of their emotions.

Socially, the skilled leader provides games and activities that encourage cooperation, stress healthy and constructive interaction, and emphasize appropriate social awareness and etiquette. Discussion of feelings, thoughts, and behaviors and how these affect one another allow children and youth to understand their social selves and to improve their social ability.

Intellectually, the adult leader provides well-organized and stimulating activities balanced with spontaneous and creative expression. The proper modeling of respect for creative and pragmatic ideas, and the presentation of games that challenge the intellectual capabilities of the group members are ways in which the skilled leader can enhance cognitive development.

Spiritually, the adult leader models a respect and reverence for all life. There is a tolerance and an understanding of the group's various religious beliefs by the leader that allows children to feel comfortable and accepted. The skilled leader provides activities that allow children and youth to discuss openly their spiritual feelings, beliefs, and experiences.

## Leadership Styles

There are three basic styles for group leaders to use: authoritarian, democratic, and laissez faire. All three styles have their place in effective group management.

The authoritarian leader takes responsibility for the group's behavior and has final authority over the group. The authoritarian leadership style is one of power and control. The authoritarian is the dispenser of power in the group.

The democratic leader relies on group input before taking action or giving direction. The leader believes that all group members should have a part in decision making. The democratic leader takes on the role of facilitator in the group.

The laissez faire leader gives no direction at all, and is the opposite of the authoritarian. Remaining aloof and often an onlooker in group activities, the laissez faire leader will take no responsibility for decision making, but allows the group to decide.

The child and youth care professional needs to acquire skills in all styles of leadership, and to develop an awareness of when to use each style. Good leadership is reflected in the adult leader's ability to guide the group. Control of the group to insure maximum safety, as well as to insure optimum enjoyment and satisfaction, is a necessary goal for the adult leader. The ability to set the mood, or to change the mood and tempo of an activity is very necessary for the smooth running of the activity. Maintenance of the health and welfare of the group can be obtained autocratically or democratically from outside or inside the group. Limits that concern safety, once established by group consensus, need to be autocratically enforced. There is no discussion or exception about the limit; it is enforced consistently. All other rules and issues are best enforced through a democratically oriented strategy. Rules, be they from a game or from group norms, attitudes, and so on, are boundaries intended to assist the group in achieving optimum satisfaction and growth.

Rules, limits, values, and morals are meant for the betterment and enrichment of human life. There is a need for leaders and members to be aware of these attitudes and behaviors, and to confront them head on if their existence is defeating group ideals. Creativity and acceptance are desirable qualities and attitudes for group interactions. These qualities cannot be dictated; therefore, a more laissez faire or democratic style is most advantageous in cultivating them in a group. Each group member requires the freedom to express his/her individuality as long as it does not impede the growth of the group. This tone of free expression allows the group members to act freely and spontaneously, without fear of jeopardizing the group or their position in the group.

## ♦ Exercise 5:1

- I would like you, the reader, to search back in your mind for a moment in order to recall memories concerning the leaders that you have known in your lifetime.
- There were some you admired and there were some you did not. Each one of those characters taught you something or many things about how to be a good leader. Allow yourself to remember, as clearly as you want to, how they looked, how they sounded, and how you felt about them.
- While doing this exercise, be sure to remember and incorporate the positive attributes they possess.
- There is a wealth of knowledge from your life experiences that will help you to formulate the positive leadership strategies that you need in order to become a successful leader. List the qualities that you feel are important to good leadership. Discuss these.

## Leadership Qualities

Effective leaders are individuals who have skills that allow them to excel as mentors, teachers, and facilitators. Child and youth care professionals must take stock of their qualities and skills and pledge to improve on them and to develop new talents that will make them effective leaders. Adult leaders must have a positive attitude, must be dependable, and must be responsible. Skilled leaders are well-organized, flexible, observant, and effective communicators. They must be able to be directive, nondirective, and democratic as the situation demands. They are facilitators of the wisdom of everyday life.

### Positive Attitude

A positive attitude needs to be projected in all areas towards the children as a group and as individuals, towards the environment and the activities as well as towards co-workers and other professionals involved in the children's lives. Group leaders are role models for the children in their group; therefore, they need to project a warm, friendly, and compassionate self that instills confidence and trust in the group members.

### Dependable

An adult leader upon whom the children can rely provides an element of personal safety and trust. A dependable leader will provide consistent limits and interventions necessary to make play safe and enjoyable. When the adult leader can be depended upon to follow through, children are able to relax and to trust that what is communicated has meaning. Dependability and trust are interdependent upon one another and, without trust, children's behavior and level of enjoyment are seriously affected.

### Responsible

Adult group leaders have the responsibility to reflect the image of individuals who take responsibility for all aspects of themselves. They are outwardly and inwardly responsible for their feelings, thoughts, and behaviors. They are responsible for the fulfillment of their wants and needs.They must be effective in conflict resolution and openly accept the consequences, both positive and negative, for their behavior. Responsible leaders are those who constantly strive towards self-awareness, self-fullfillment, and self-responsibility.

## ♦ Exercise 5:2

- Ask yourself the following questions:
- When I express feelings and opinions, do I speak in general terms, or do I speak about myself specifically?
- Do I satisfy my wants and needs by actively pursuing and achieving my goals; or, do I wait passively to have my needs met?
- When faced with a problem, do I confront the issues, and try to come to an appropriate resolution; or, do I not act and hope it will resolve itself?
- Do I find myself blaming others or events for my misfortunes; or, do I take responsibility for my own choices?
- Do I rely on mind reading and anticipating behavior in order to appreciate how I affect others?

- Do I check out my behavior by asking for feedback and clarification?
- Am I able to accept the positive strokes that others give to me or, do I discount what they have said?
- Do I find myself rescuing others when they get into trouble; or, do I support that person's efforts to solve their own problems?
- Write down the answers to these questions and share them with someone you trust.

### Organized and Flexible

The adult leader needs to have activities and games well-planned and organized. The organization should also allow for some flexibility and creative expression. The adult leader should have clear goals and objectives in mind. Difficult tasks should be broken down into easy steps. The well-organized leader also knows how to access necessary resources and knows where these resources are at all times.

### Skilled Observer

Children are constantly communicating to each other non-verbally. They also send messages to the observer about their emotional state. A skilled observer with a sound knowledge of child development can interpret non-verbal messages and react to messages called "clue behavior" that transmit states of emotionality. Clue behavior is not difficult to read, but is often idiosyncratic. This requires a knowledge of, and a relationship with, each child. The child and youth care professional who is able to decode these messages by watching and obtaining verbal feedback from the child can anticipate problems and put interventions in place that will remedy the situation. For example, Molly's behavior at morning recess had been very sporadic for the past two months. It seemed that one day she would isolate herself, having nothing to do with the group games; other days,she would become totally involved; at other times, she would be physically aggressive by hitting and by pushing the other children. This sporadic behavior was noticed only at morning recess; at other times, Molly was very involved and well-behaved at game time. Cathy had been observing this behavior very closely for the past week, and had been talking with Molly before and after morning recess. Then, suddenly, during one of their talks, Molly had mentioned that her Mom had changed shifts at work, and that the babysitter was coming in the morning to get her ready for school.

After some further investigation, Cathy was able to decode Molly's clue behavior. The babysitter was insisting that Molly finish her breakfast before she went to school. Molly resented the babysitter being there, and wanted her mother there in the mornings because that was their time to talk. Molly was missing these talks and as an act of defiance, was throwing her breakfast in the garbage and not eating anything, except for the times when the babysitter sat and ate with Molly. A quick call to Molly's mother corrected the situation. Molly's mother rescheduled her time so that she and Molly could have some quiet time in the evening, and the babysitter was instructed to sit and have breakfast with Molly. Molly's nutritional and emotional needs were not being met and she was acting out at school; this was something that neither she nor the adults in her life were aware of. The clues for these needs came out in her behavior. Some clue behavior is obvious and other behavior is very subtle, and requires keen observation and investigation. When this behavior is observed and responded to, children's play needs less behavioral intervention. In many cases this responsiveness can have ramifications on other areas of the child's life.

## Effective Communicator

The adult group leader requires skill in both listening and communicating. Language needs to be clearly articulated and to be appropriate to the age grouping of the group participants. Language needs to be congruent in that the verbal portion of the message needs to coincide with the non-verbal portion of the message.Language should reflect the three main sensory modalities. The use of visual, auditory, and kinesthetic (tactile/emotional) language increases the chances that all participants will appreciate the message communicated.

Communication should not be judgmental, analytical, or critical. It should reflect an accepting attitude. Instructions, praise, and other important communications can be repeated to insure clear understanding. The onus is on the group leader to insure that all group members have heard and understood the communication.

Positive listening requires the group leader to listen intently to the communicator; when appropriate, the communication can be paraphrased to gain clarification. Feedback to the communicator in the form of non-verbal and verbal communication will assist the sender in feeling understood. Verbal feedback like asking for clarification or verbalizing that you understand, and non-verbal feedback like nodding your head, smiling, and making eye contact can assist the communicator in feeling understood.

## ♦ Exercise 5:3

- Read through the following list of suggestions that concern positive communication styles.
- Make a list of the areas that you feel that you need to improve upon.
- Write down a number of strategies that you could begin to implement in the future to improve your communication skills.
- *Quality of Language:*
- Choose your words carefully; say what you really mean. Do not use slang. Do not talk down to experts and do not talk over the heads of beginners in terms of your choice of words and terminology.
- *Clear Expression of Ideas:*
- Organize your ideas beforehand. Express your ideas in a logical sequence. Use complete sentences with one idea per sentence. Stick to your purpose (don't ramble or get off topic).

- *Voice Production:*
- Vary the tone of your voice (avoid using a monotone). Speak with an adequate amount of volume. Vary the pace at which you speak but guard against speaking too slowly or too quickly (most of us speak faster than we realize). Open your mouth; avoid mumbling.
- *Body Language:*
- Project an "open" appearance (arms and legs uncrossed, relaxed). Watch what you do with your hands (are they covering your mouth, are they playing nervously with a pen or coins in your pocket?). Make eye contact with your listeners. Does your body language match what you are saying? Try not to give conflicting messages. Body language makes up approximately seventy percent of our overall communication. Fifty percent of this body language is communicated by the face.
- *Courtesy:*
- Phrase your ideas, questions, answers, etc. as politely as you can. Be careful not to interrupt others. Be a good listener as well as a good speaker.

## Behavioral Manager

The adult leader must continually refine and test behavior management skills. All of the qualities mentioned above are necessary for good group behavior management. This book has sound, time-tested behavioral strategies scattered throughout its pages. A major part of the success of group behavior management is found in a well-planned program. When all the elements of good programming are met and adhered to, behavior management, in most cases, is not necessary. When each child is recognized and encouraged as an individual and as a group member by the group leader, behavior management becomes much easier. When a child needs to be reminded of the rules or needs to take a time-out, this is not a punishment; this should be presented as a positive strategy out of concern for the individual. For example, John has been acting very impulsively in the group game. He is pushing others, falling over his own feet, and grabbing the ball from others. Mary has cautioned the group as a whole with "Gently, gently," in a concerned voice, as well as "Careful, children, careful, John!" but has not given John enough support because he is still acting impulsively. Mary moves closer to John, places her hands on his shoulders, and squats down so that she can talk face to face with him. "John, I want you to sit down and catch your breath. You're looking all flushed in the face. Are you hot?" John gestures that he is. She continues,"Sit down and close your eyes and concentrate. Slow yourself down until you feel centered again. You know how you felt that day when we were doing yoga and you said 'I feel all cool inside'? Well, just like that! Let yourself feel all cool inside and then, when you're finished, come and touch my hand, okay?" John sits down and makes himself feel cool. In a few minutes, John comes back, looking more relaxed, and he touches Mary's hand. Mary gives John a big smile, a gentle touch, and some encouragement to re-enter the game.

Behavior management should not be intrusive, and this requires a sound knowledge of appropriate behavior and a solid relationship with the child. At times, adult leaders have expectations that date back to their past experiences; they might not be appropriate for children today. Therefore it is essential that child and youth care professionals continually upgrade their skills as a behavioural manager.

## ♦ Exercise 5:4

- Think back to the leaders you have had in the past.
- When did you feel that they were being too punitive, too restrictive, or too old-fashioned in their approach?
- If you are having trouble with this part, think of the leaders that you have in your life in the present and ask the same question.
- In most cases, your feelings were probably correct because many adults were raised in punitive systems where all behavior would be punished and rules for conduct were strict and not child oriented.
- Go back now to the situations that you recalled and decide how it could have been handled to your satisfaction.
- Get to know your children and try to eliminate rules and expectations that you have for them that are unrealistic, outdated, punitive, or unnecessary, and those that are just no fun.
- If the game or activity being presented to the children requires a lot of behavioral intervention on the part of the adult leader, perhaps the group is not ready for this activity or game. The adult group leader needs to be

aware that punishment serves the adult's need to control but, in most cases, does not serve the needs of the child.

### Facilitator

When given a leadership role, we often do just that, lead. Leading is important; however, often children need the adult to step out of the group and to facilitate. This means changing from the person who controls the activity to someone who has instigated it and now watches or who has merely suggested that play is appropriate now and then sits back and observes. A facilitator allows the children to lead and is present to insure emotional and physical safety. The leader becomes observer and is no longer part of the group.

This facilitation sets the stage for spontaneity, creativity, shared leadership and social learning. This facilitation role is the final evolution of the adult group leader. When the child and youth care professional can allow the group to function on its own with very little intervention then the task as group facilitator is complete. This stage does not come without a lot of hard work and a great deal of practising the aforementioned qualities as well as a solid understanding of child development and group behavior.

## Developing Leaders in Children's Groups

Once the child and youth care professional has established the role as adult group leader, the ultimate aim should be to evolve out of this role. The evolution allows natural leaders as well as the leadership potential in all children to emerge. The group's evolutionary process to the ideal of shared leadership and cooperation is shaped by this transference of power. The child and youth care professional not only needs to become a skilled leader but also needs to be able to develop this quality in others. Recognition of emerging leaders in the group is the first step in the transference of power. Identification of these leaders is important because it recognizes the present stage in the group's process and joins, rather than resists, its evolutionary pace. Through keen observation, these leaders can be identified. Group members will often maintain more eye contact with these children in order to pick up non-verbal cues from them. Natural leaders often initiate free play activities, settle disputes among members, speak first or last in group discussions, and provide solutions to group problems. The child may be leading in a negative way and, often, the adult leader's first inclination is to suppress this child. However, this child may very well be the key to the success of the program.

Once these leaders begin to appear, they need to be given leadership roles and responsibilities as early as possible. By singling these children out, their leadership is recognized or affirmed by the adult leader. It also is the course of least resistance when trying to establish your credibility among the group members. During group activities they can be asked to pass out equipment, to choose teams, to invent or teach a new game to the group, to help set up for the game, and to assist with any other means of leading. Once their leadership is recognized or established, these natural leaders will feel more comfortable when other group members take on leadership roles.

Also, the group members will feel more comfortable and less anxious with having to compete with these sometimes powerful leaders in order to lead in the group. Once the atmosphere is established and the group feels safe, appropriate leadership skills can be practiced and enjoyed by all group members. Some children are better leaders than others and some, perhaps, are not meant to be leaders. All children can learn from the experience and can develop an appreciation for what it is like to lead as well as to follow. The most effective way to develop positive leadership abilities is to model those desirable qualities for all members to observe.

Leaders often emerge from games that challenge the group's ability to work together. These types of leaders are usually good problem solvers and efficient organizers. Their skills can be singled out and recognized during feedback sessions or during group discussions.

Leaders also emerge on the playground when everyone is bored. These leaders are usually the creative group members who have unique ideas and ways of presenting them that spark the group's fantasy world. Their skills are also important to point out to the group, as their talents can be very useful.

Leaders emerge during times of stress to comfort and to soften the emotional burdens of the group. These are the humanitarians of the group who are in touch with their emotional selves. Their contribution also needs to be recognized by the adult leader and in time they need to be appreciated by the group members.

Leaders appear when their talents and abilities are well suited for the activity; for example, athletic ability in team sports. These children can show leadership and instill confidence in team members. Once again, their talents should be recognized and valued by the group.

Leaders emerge when group morale is low and when motivation levels and energy levels are spent. They are often comical leaders and, in some cases, charismatic leaders who help the group rise above its depression. Their skills are very valuable to the group at both a task and maintenance level.

## Negative Leading

When children in the group try to influence the other group members to be uncooperative or to be physically or emotionally hurtful to the leader or others in the group, they are endangering themselves and the other group members. They are leading or are attempting to lead the group in a negative direction. This type of leading is not to be tolerated and must be stopped quickly. The group needs to know that this type of interaction is not healthy and will not be encouraged or fostered in the group setting. There are often some negative interactions that are borderline; that is, they are not destructive enough to be overtly harmful, yet they are not positive either. These behaviors are best dealt with outside the larger group and can be discussed with the child after the group has finished. The incidents of negative leading can primarily be dealt with by a word or two to the offender and then, some positive feedback or encouragement given shortly after. If the behavior continues, a mild confrontation as to why the child is continuing the behavior is required. Stay away from judging the child and from using putdowns. Body contact, for example, a hand on the shoulder, can be beneficial. If the behavior continues, the child must be timed out or asked to leave until that child is able to establish the necessary controls in order to behave appropriately in the group.

Group leadership is the rock on which the profession of child and youth care is built and the establishment of these skills are of primary importance in the delivery of optimum care and education.

> **The provision of limits and structure are vital in creating a framework for freedom.**
>
> **JUDITH RUBIN**

### Bibliography for LEADERSHIP

Carkhuff, R. (1987). *The art of helping VI.* Amherst, MA: Human Resource Development.

Elkind, D. (1981). *The hurried child.* Toronto: Addison-Wesley.

Henry, J. (1980). *A scientist in American life.* Washington, DC: Smithsonian Institute Press.

Miller, S., Nunnally, E., & Wackman, D. (1979) *Talking together.* Minneapolis, MN: Interpersonal Communication.

Satir, V. (1972). *Peoplemaking.* Palo Alto, CA: Science and Behavior Books.

Sayles, L. (1979). *Leadership: What effective managers really do and how they do it.* New York: McGraw-Hill.

Redl, F. (1966). *When we deal with children.* New York: The Free Press.

Rubin, J. (1984). *Child art therapy.* New York: Van Nostrand Reinhold Company.

CHAPTER SIX

# RAPPORT AND RELATIONSHIPS

When I close my eyes and relax, I can still hear my grandmother's words.

"In the early dawn breeze, a tiny maple key propels itself to its new earthen home." She told this story to me many times. "Moisture, soil, air, and the gifts of the sun are the elements necessary to its survival. This tiny seed gives birth to living splendor, like the trees in our back yard. This new creation, in turn, gives of itself to the birds, small animals, and insects of the world as they make it their home. The tiny seed develops in relationship to its environment which nourishes it into a magnificent tree that shelters and protects." Grandma was a wise woman and she taught me many things, but the story of that small seed giving life to so many wondrous things was my greatest lesson.

**Letting people in is largely a matter of not expending energy to keep them out.**

**HUGH PRATHER**

Rapport, that first feeling of trust and respect, like a tiny seed when it is nurtured by its environment, gives birth to a healthy relationship and that healthy relationship, in turn, provides the child with opportunities to grow and to flourish. In order to nurture these young saplings, it is imperative that child and youth care professionals master techniques that will contribute to the cultivation of positive relationships with the children in their care. Quick and efficient rapport-building strategies, as well as the skills necessary for the development of solid relationships, are the necessary elements that nourish all children, even those whose environments and life experiences have made it difficult for them to grow. This chapter points out the interrelatedness of rapport and relationship development. It will focus, identify, and make available, through discussion and group exercises, those elements and strategies conducive to developing rapport and, thus, it will promote solid, healthy relationships.

## Personal Awareness

Self-awareness, for child and youth care professionals, is basic to their ability to form meaningful relationships with children in their care. Child and youth care professionals should have a sound knowledge of their individual strengths and weaknesses, an awareness of their behavior patterns and behavioral strategies, and an understanding of how they were nurtured as children, in order to work through roadblocks that hamper effective rapport building. Attitudes toward helping, and the need to help children, must be explored in order to ensure that a healthy focus is maintained. Effective care givers must maintain an air of genuineness that can only come from a great deal of personal awareness. There are several ways for child and youth care professionals to gain a better understanding of themselves. One way is to find a reputable counsellor/therapist and ask for assistance; also, many books have been written that provide strategies for self-exploration. A support system of friends with whom to discuss personal problems, and to provide emotional support, can also give insight. These support systems also help to keep the child care professional healthy in times of stress.

## ♦ Exercise 6:1

- Make yourself as comfortable as you can, set down your book and let your mind drift for thirty seconds.
- Allow yourself to feel more relaxed with the passing of each second.
- First of all, visualize your present self,
- your physical self,
- your emotional self,
- your spiritual self,
- and your intellectual self.
- Try to get a clear representation of these in your mind.
- How does each image fit with your self-concept?
- Visualize in your mind the way you imagine others see you.
- Now imagine the ideal self, the self you aspire to be, a realistic and healthy image of your potential self.
- Now, visualize an image of yourself reaching your potential in the following areas:
- your physical self,
- your intellectual self,
- your spiritual self,
- your emotional self,
- and your social self.
- Hold out your hands now, palm side up,
- imagine the self that you are right now in the palm of your hand, and
- sustain this visual representation of the you that you are right now.
- In your left palm, imagine the image of you as your ideal self.
- Now, compare the two images.
- Ask yourself what needs to change in order for the present self to be more like the ideal self.
- Be aware of necessary changes and begin to picture yourself as the ideal you.
- Slowly bring your two hands together and hold them there. Take ten seconds to strengthen your vision of your ideal image.
- Relax and focus your attention back to the here and now.
- Discuss your experience or write about it in your journal.

## Self-Esteem

When developing relationships with children, the individual child's feelings of self-worth must always be kept at the forefront of any strategy. A clear message of total acceptance needs to be projected by the child and youth care professional at all times. This total acceptance, however, does not mean tolerance of negative behavior. When the child's behavior is unacceptable this needs to be communicated. It should not reflect negatively in any way on the child's feelings of self-worth. The behavior may be unacceptable but the child is lovable and capable. Punishment, ridicule, and other forms of negative discipline should not be used; the negative effect of these methods on the child's self-esteem, and on relationships within the group, can be serious. Positive reinforcement, through praise, and redirection of negative behavior, provides the child with the necessary elements to control individual behavior. Construction of appropriate environments and activities that promote positive behavior should be routine considerations when working with children in a group or individually. When the child feels valued by the child and youth care professional, and when the child is able to trust that professional, self-esteem will grow. This elevated feeling of self-importance will usually provide the child with the strength necessary to follow rules, and to interact positively in relationships with others.

### ♦ Exercise 6:2

- Take a personal inventory of your strengths and list them on a sheet of paper, leaving plenty of space between each one.
- Elaborate on this list, taking one strength at a time and list what activities and behaviors promote this strength.
- Now you have a list of things to do to nurture yourself.
- Make a similar list for a friend or loved one. In what behaviors or activities do you see these strengths manifesting themselves? Share your list.
- Make a list of your three biggest weaknesses.
- Find out more about these three by answering questions such as: When do they happen most often?
- Why?
- Where do these things most often occur?
- With whom do they happen most often?

- Decide if you want to change any of these weaknesses, or if you are happy with them?
- If you're feeling courageous, list three more.
- Make note of the times when you discount or put yourself down,
- or your environment,
- or your friends.
- Now make a corresponding list of times when you praise or appreciate yourself, your friends or your environment.
- If you feel compelled to be negative, be compelled also to give the positive side as much time and energy.
- Become aware and vigilant of your personal needs and of those of your loved ones.
- Your responsibility is to meet your own needs and to provide opportunities for those you love to have some of their needs met through you. List those needs you have the most difficulty meeting.
- Who could assist you in meeting these needs?
- Do something good for yourself everyday. You owe it to the rest of the world to set an example of how to treat yourself with care.

## Touch

Marasmus, a failure to thrive, is a disease that ravaged orphanages, hospitals, and institutions during the nineteenth and early twentieth centuries. This disease was lethal and when translated literally it means wasting away. The child would lose weight and appetite until it died. The cause of this disease was the lack of physical contact from other humans. Everyone needs to be touched, stroked, cuddled, fondled, and held. Without this tactile stimulation, children and adults do not grow in a healthy way. Their emotional selves grow gnarled, crooked, bent, and deformed. They can be smoothed, straightened, and supported by touch. The ever-increasing realization of the extent of physical and sexual abuse, in the field of child and youth care has thrown many agencies and professionals into a panic. Lawsuits and allegations have marred the reputations of workers and agencies. Some institutions, especially those servicing the adolescent and pre-adolescent population, have passed sanctions against child and youth care professionals hugging and holding the youth in their care. The tragic irony of this situation is that children and youth in care need touch to get well; yet, their healers have their hands tied. Children, with few exceptions, have a strong need for physical contact and, for some, this is their primary mode of learning. They need to touch and to be touched in order to understand. Children under stress require more physical contact than usual. The child and youth care professional's task is to guide the child towards appropriate and inappropriate ways of fulfilling this sometimes ravenous need. Once a positive relationship has been established, all children benefit from appropriate physical contact. Each child requires varying degrees of touch. An environment where open and honest physical contact is provided allows each child to fulfill his/her needs from whomever or whatever is appropriate. Physical contact, for those children who are hypersensitive to touch, should be administered slowly and monitored until the child is comfortable with being touched. Cases of hypersensitivity in children and youth should always be treated under the care of a team of professionals. Among different cultures, families, groups, and pairs, physical contact is enjoyed and transmitted in a wide variety of healthy and wholesome ways. Touch is a very powerful and a very personal way of developing trust.

## Communication

Communication is affected by how, what, when, where, and why something is said. Its outcome depends heavily upon the nature of the past and present experiences of the receiver. Factors such as voice tone, tempo, diction, hand gestures, body position, eye contact, temperature and humidity, emotional status, social status, sex, age, and maturity of speakers, as well as the words themselves, their syntax, semantics, and their understood meanings, all make up the complex process of verbal and non-verbal communication. When child and youth care professionals take time to analyze and improve their communication skills, their effectiveness and their influence with children increases. The messages we send verbally and non-verbally form the basis of all social relationships. The importance of language cannot be stressed enough. Its implications and various levels of complexity need to be seriously considered. Non-verbal communications carry four times the conversational weight of verbal messages when both are used in language. Therefore, it is most useful to consider what is being communicated non-verbally to children. Personal awareness of how the child and youth care professional communicates non-verbally, and an appreciation of what constitutes non-verbal language, will assist in the development of effective communication skills.

## ♦ Exercise 6:3

- The following is a useful exercise that will help child and youth care professionals to get in touch with factors that influence non-verbal communication. You are encouraged to try it now, and most importantly, to try it just before coming into contact with the children in your care.
- Ask yourself the following: "How am I feeling about myself, mentally, physically, spiritually, and emotionally, today?"
- What are my relationships with my significant others like?
- What are my feelings about the children, collectively and individually?
- How do I feel about my co-workers, supervisors, and/or administrators?
- Do I need to communicate any of my feelings to the children or staff members?
- Am I prepared to work in the present today, or will the past and future be foremost in my mind?
- Once dressed and ready for work, find a full length mirror. Stand in front of the mirror and ask yourself: What messages am I communicating through my appearance, my hair style, clothing, shoes, etc.?
- Do I like what I see?
- Can I say to myself "I love you"?
- What changes, additions, subtractions can I make right now to make a difference?
- These exercises can be performed every day. They only take a few minutes and they contain very important information to be aware of when working with children and youth.

## Physical Boundaries

Most humans have an imaginary boundary around their person. This boundary is determined by the distance between themselves and the person with whom they are communicating. There is a distance that is maintained when speaking with casual acquaintances; it is quite different from the distance we physically maintain when we are speaking with intimate friends. This space can be termed a personal boundary. There are other boundaries in relationship to touch and physical proximity and they correspond to the person's personal boundary.

There is a socially appropriate distance that all people maintain between one another whenever possible. Children are sometimes not given proper respect in terms of their personal boundaries. Child and youth care professionals need to be aware of this need within the child. Permission to cross this boundary is most often given non-verbally; however, when in doubt, it is best to ask for permission. Children, in turn, can be taught to set boundaries and limits for their physical selves. Some cultures dictate that personal space is large, and other cultures require a small personal space. This is an important consideration when dealing with children.

### ♦ Exercise 6:4

- Imagine a close or intimate friend.
- Recall the ease in which you both cross over each other's personal physical boundaries.
- Now imagine someone with whom you have a more formal relationship, e.g., an instructor, the librarian, or a store clerk. Try to sense how you would feel if they crossed over your personal boundaries.

## Sensory Awareness and Preferred Modalities

An awareness of sensory modalities can also be useful when attempting to develop rapport and to strengthen relationships with children. All of the information and experiences perceived by humans are represented by one or more of the five senses. All experience past, present, internal, or external can be categorized in terms of whether they primarily involve seeing, hearing, feeling, tasting, and smelling. Children, like all humans, have a stronger or more dominant sense which they use and rely upon more frequently. This is their preferred modality. Some children rely more heavily on their visual modality to make sense of their worlds. This can mean they are more affected by, or concerned with, what they see, both internally in the mind's eye and externally. Other children rely more heavily on what they hear; they use their auditory modality more frequently. This preferred modality can be identified in a number of ways and by various techniques (Dilts, Bandler, Bandler-Cameron, DeLozier, & Grinder, 1980). Some children may rely on their kinesthetic modality, which means that they feel externally by using their sense of touch, and that they feel internally by experiencing and re-experiencing their emotions in order to best understand their worlds. The sense of smell and the sense of taste are extremely powerful and useful in the early stages of development but, as the child gets older, they are not as frequently used as are the auditory, kinesthetic, and visual modalities.

## ♦ Exercise 6:5

- Think about yourself for a moment. Do you prefer to be given directions to a friend's house orally, or will a map drawn on a piece of paper be better? (Ideally both would be better, but if you had to have one or the other, which one would you choose?)
- Someone who prefers to have the directions told to them or written on a piece of paper are more apt to rely on their auditory system.
- If the preference is on the map, the person is likely visually oriented.
- When learning a new skill, do you benefit from trial and error experimental learning?
- Those of us who prefer trial and error learning may rely more heavily on our kinesthetic (touch and emotion) sense.
- When meeting people for the first time, do you attend more to what the person says, and the sound of their voice, to how they look, or to how they make you feel (i.e., your "gut feeling" about them)?
- Are you more visually, auditorily or kinesthetically oriented? Think about other behaviors (e.g., the type of language you use).
- Is it kinesthetically, visually, or auditorily oriented?

## Identifying the Preferred Modality

Children display characteristics that make their preferred sensory modality identifiable (Barbe, 1982). Visual children organize their world by means of what they see and what they perceive visually; they tend to speak using predominantly visual words (Bandler & Grinder, 1976). For example, "*Look*, you can *see* the sailboats really *clearly* now, Dad. *Notice* all the *colored angles* near the bow. What a *sight*!" These children are often more concerned with their appearance. They also tend to do better in mathematics, as opposed to reading and spelling. Visual imagery is often more easily attainable for these children, and they frequently have vivid and colorful dreams. A visual child often needs to *see* something before believing it to be true and, therefore, understands best when shown how to accomplish particular tasks. Visual children may tend to look at the person who is speaking more often than other children (Barbe, 1982).

Auditory children, on the other hand, will speak using words that predominantly relate to sound (Bandler & Grinder, 1976). For example, "It *sounds* to me like she won't *listen* to what you're *saying* to her. I think she has *turned you off*." These children are real "talkers" and tend to speak early in their development. Their voice tone is apt to give indications of their moods. Their tempo when speaking is often very rhythmic. Reading and spelling are favourite subjects in school, and auditory children may do poorly in math. Auditory children learn best when given verbal instructions, and can often listen very well when they appear to be inattentive (Barbe, 1982).

Kinesthetic children learn best through their sense of touch and their emotions. They speak most often in feeling words (Bandler & Grinder, 1976). For example, "I have a *feeling* that if he does not get in *touch* with what's *bugging* him, we are all in for a *rough* time." These children may be labelled "clingers" or "huggers" due to their strong need for physical contact. They are often considered "sloppy" since they pay more attention to how their clothes feel than how they look. Their voice pitch is slightly lower than visual and auditory children. A kinesthetic child is often the child who is labelled emotional. They use a lot of hand gestures when speaking, and often count on their fingers (Barbe, 1982). These children do well in projects that require making things with their hands. Kinesthetic children usually enjoy crafts and body contact sports.

It is important to note that the above profiles of visual, auditory, and kinesthetic children are not foolproof and, like all categories and stages, the child and youth care professional must be aware of the child's individuality. However, children presenting profiles similar to the ones outlined above can be hypothesized as being either visual, auditory, or kinesthetic.

## Developing Rapport Through the Preferred Modality

### Visual children

Speak to this child using visual language. Whenever possible, include a visual representation of what you are communicating. Be aware of your physical appearance and how you appear to this child. Be very careful of incongruent messages, e.g., when your words and body posture do not match. Painting, drawing, picture books, photography, television, and computers are some of the activities preferred by visual children.

### Auditory children

These children like to be spoken to and to be permitted to talk things out. They respond best to auditory language. Voice tone and tempo, as well as inflection, can be very important when trying to effectively communicate. Tape recorders, records, songs, and telephones are some of the activities enjoyed by the auditory child.

### Kinesthetic children

The sense of touch and physical closeness are very often important to these types of children. A handshake, a pat on the back, or a hug are effective ways of communicating acceptance to kinesthetic children. When communicating verbally, use feeling and tactile words; some type of physical contact is helpful as well. Kinesthetic children like to be in touch with what they are experiencing. Back rubs, wrestling, clay, and drama are some very effective ways to encourage and stimulate kinesthetically oriented children.

## ♦ Exercise 6:6

♦ Reflecting is a form of "pacing" (Bandler & Grinder, 1976) or "mirroring" and is literally imitating or miming the child's behavior. This technique is probably the most effective way of establishing quick rapport, and it is the one used either consciously or unconsciously by most child and youth care professionals. Try this technique on a child or unsuspecting friend.

- Observe the child, paying particular attention to the child's posture and facial expression.
- Recreate or imitate the child's posture and expression. Take on the mirror image of the child, and visualize the child in your mind.
- Clues and symbols abound in using visualization. Mentally record your experience.
- When the child moves, changing posture and expression, you follow, mirroring the child. As this mirroring is taking place, be aware of any emotions or physical sensations (e.g., feeling of anger, muscle tension) that you experience while reflecting the child.

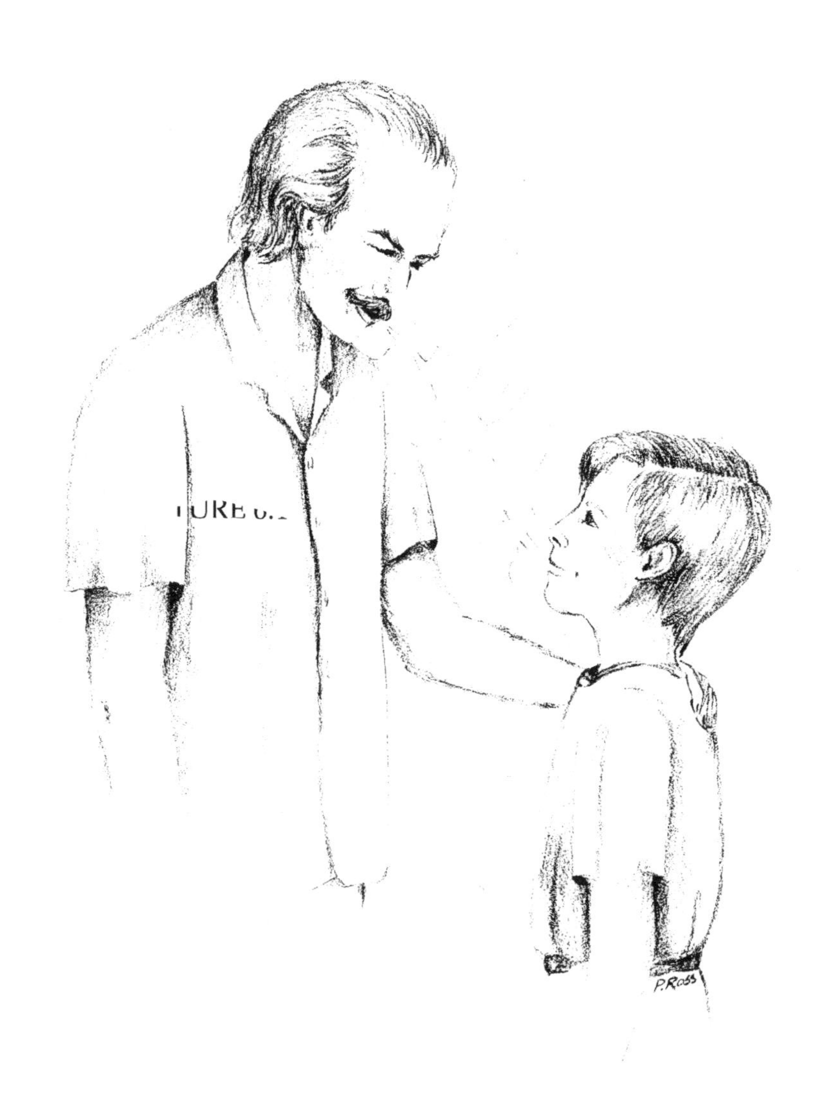

- Having successfully mirrored the child's posture and expression, begin to use word phrases similar to those used by the child. Match the child's language by responding with visual words when the child uses visual language; use auditory words when the child uses auditory language; and similarly, employ kinesthetic, olfactory, and gustatory language where the child does.
- When you have successfully mirrored and feel comfortable with mirroring the child's language, observe some of the child's more subtle non-verbal behaviors, e.g., breathing depth and rate, gestures and mannerisms, eye and head movements, etc.
- You can then mirror one or more of these subtle behaviors.
- As the child changes behaviors, follow by matching them.
- Become aware of emotions and physical sensations taking place in your body as you mirror the child.
- Having successfully mirrored the more subtle non-verbal behaviors, you can now mirror the more subtle verbal behaviors, e.g., voice tone and tempo,inflections, pronunciations, etc.
- Next you might discuss with the child the accuracy of your predicted awareness of the child's emotional state. For example, the child who is tense and fidgety just before going into class might be asked, "You're feeling nervous about going into math class?" If the child confirms this, the adult might respond with, "Math makes you nervous?" and so on. Through this process, the child has feelings identified, and feels understood at an emotional level.
- These steps may be repeated several times during an interaction with a child. It is important not to mimic the child in an obvious way which might make the child feel self-conscious or agitated. A more subtle and unintrusive style of communication is most effective here. It is through this mirroring process that the child and youth care professional begins to appreciate more fully the child's experience. The child experiences comfort and understanding by experiencing, consciously and unconsciously, this mirroring process; thus, the child feels more relaxed, validated, and understood.

## Developmental Stages

In developing rapport and in strengthening relationships with children, it is most beneficial to have an awareness of their normal growth and development. Developmental stages will be continually emphasized throughout this text. A complete knowledge and firm understanding of the patterns in the normal growth and development process is essential to successful child and youth care. Child and youth care professionals should always be cognizant of the physical, social, emotional, intellectual, and language developmental level of each child. This information better equips them to assist each child to progress and develop at a suitable rate. A complete understanding and appreciation requires hours of studying and of observing normal and atypical growth and development. This topic cannot be dealt with here, in the detail it deserves, but readers are encouraged to consult books or take courses on developmental psychology. For a brief outline of developmental needs, refer to Chapter 3, Program Design. Always keep in mind that no one individual child follows perfectly any of the developmental stages presently known to the psychological world (Mussen, Conger, & Kagan, 1969). The way the child progresses through stages of development, and the way in which common patterns of behavioral, emotional, and cognitive development are expressed, vary according to the child's individuality and life situation (Ames & Ilg, 1955). When individual differences are considered, however, understanding these levels can serve to assist child and youth care professionals in terms of establishing closeness to the children in their care.

## Rapport and Relationship in the Group Setting

Most of the strategies discussed earlier in this chapter are easily adaptable to a group setting. It is ideal when the child and youth care professional is able to meet with each child individually in order to form a basic rapport before the child enters into the group situation. This is not always possible, so it is up to the professional to find appropriate opportunities to develop and to strengthen rapport with the individuals who do not seem especially responsive to the group setting. This can be done before or after the group meets or during pairing exercises in the group process. Children in groups need to develop rapport with one another; this group rapport is essential to the success and productivity of the group. The child and youth care professional can assist in providing the children with opportunities to form healthy and productive relationships as outlined in the preceding chapters.

**Personal experience is a synthesis of sensory emotional experience, and out of it thought emerges.**

**ALICE YARDLEY**

## Bibliography for RAPPORT AND RELATIONSHIPS

Ames, L., & Ilg, F. (1955). *Child behaviour from birth to ten*. New York: Harper and Row.

Bandler, R., & Grinder, J. (1976). *The structure of magic II*. Palo Alto, CA: Science and Behavior Books.

Barbe, W. (June, 1982). *What we know about modality*. Paper given at the 25th Council for Exceptional Children, Chicago.

Burns, M. (1984). Rapport and relationships: The basis of child care. *Journal of Child Care, 22*(2), 47–56.

Dilts, R., Bandler, R., Bandler-Cameron, L., DeLozier, J., & Grinder, J. (1980). *Neuro-linguistic programming* (Vol. 1). Cupertino, CA: Meta Publications.

Mussen, P., Conger, J., & Kagan, J. (1969). *Child development and personality*. New York: Harper and Row.

Prather, H. (1981). *A book of games*. New York: Doubleday.

Yardley, A. (1988). *Senses and sensitivity*. London: Rubicon Publishing.

# THE PRACTICE

# ACTIVITIES

CHAPTER SEVEN

# BRIDGES AND ANCHOR POINTS

Games and activities have a wide variety of uses. Included are several games that show how games can be used to help others to adjust to difficult situations and to cope more effectively in their daily routines.

Bridges are games or activities that make transitional periods (times when a child is between routines or changing from one environment to another, e.g., getting ready for bed), easier to cope with for both the child and the youth care professional. Bridges span the gap between one activity and another.

Anchor points are games or activities that relax and center the child or youth in order for them to regain equilibrium. Sometimes it is one to one, sometimes it is forming a circle, sometimes it is playing a guessing game; all of the time, it is familiar and reminds the participant of good times.

When the children and youth are waiting in line for tickets, travelling in the car, between homework and supper or when they have ten minutes before recess, bridges help to settle themselves emotionally and to occupy themselves cognitively through difficult situations and times of insecurity.

When children and youth are feeling distraught or unsettled, behaving negatively or withdrawn, anchor points can lift their spirits, change their behavior, their thinking, and their emotions.

## Group Activities

### ♦ WAITING

Close your eyes, relax and pick out ten different sounds. Count the sounds on your fingers, one at a time. When you are finished, open your eyes. Discuss with the group the different sounds.

Look around you and find ten different signs. Count them on your fingers, one at a time. When you are finished, close your eyes. Discuss the different signs with the group.

Get in touch with your environment and feel the different textures or sensations. Count them on your fingers, one at a time and when you are finished, put your hands on your hips. Discuss the different tactile experiences.

### ♦ TWENTY QUESTIONS

Each group member takes a turn choosing a specific person, place or thing that is generally known to the rest of the group, i.e., Martin Luther King, Rocky Mountains, baseball glove, etc.

The group is allowed to ask up to twenty questions that require a yes or no answer in order to guess the person, place or thing.

### ♦ I SPY

This is an old favourite and can be used for colours, sounds, beginning letter of the word, etc.

"I spy with my little eye something that is red."

"I hear with my little ear something that sounds like hiss."

"I spy with my little eye something that begins with a."

Try to invent one of your own versions of "I Spy."

### ♦ ROCK, SCISSORS, PAPER

This game is played in twos and threes and thus, can be played with any number of participants.

This hand game is played by participants on the count of three: holding out either a clenched fist, two fingers or an open hand. A clenched fist signifies a rock, two fingers signifies scissors and an open hand signifies paper. The game centers on the concept that a rock *smashes* scissors,

scissors *cut* paper, and paper *wraps around* a rock. The game is scored by rock defeats scissors, scissors defeat paper, and paper defeats rock.

## ♦ ONE, TWO, THREE

This is an odd or even game played with three players. As in Rock, Scissors, Paper, the three players move fists up and down and on the count of three, show one or two fingers. The odd man out scores the point.

## ♦ MIND READING

The same format as One, Two, Three, except the three or more players are trying to read each other's minds so that they will all put out the same number of fingers: all ones or all twos. When they succeed, they all receive a point.

## ♦ ODD OR EVEN

One player chooses Odd and the other chooses Even. As in One, Two, Three, on the count of three, the player puts out one or two fingers. If the sum total is odd, the Odd player scores, but if they are even, the Even player scores.

## ♦ HULL GULL

Player has an object that will fit easily in one hand. The opponent has to guess which hand has the object.

## ♦ ELECTRICITY

The group holds hands and one person is asked to set the charge off. The player does this by squeezing the hand of the person on the right. This player in turn squeezes the hand of the person on the right. The electrical current runs around the group.

## ♦ BUZZ

The word Buzz is inserted when a certain number comes up when the group is counting, e.g., three. The first player says, one, the second player says, two, and the third player says Buzz (instead of three). Each time the number three comes up as the group continues the count, i.e., twelve, Buzz, fourteen. Another way is to insert the word Buzz for multiples of the number, i.e., multiples seven; six, Buzz, eight, nine, ten, eleven, twelve, thirteen, Buzz, fifteen, sixteen, seventeen, eighteen, nineteen, Twenty, Buzz, etc.

## ♦ THE MINISTER'S CAT

This is an alphabet game. "The Minister's Cat is a ________________ cat." The blank has to be filled with an adjective that starts with the next letter of the alphabet, e.g., an **a**nnoying cat; a **b**ig cat; a **c**razy cat.

Next, the group can add two adjectives, e.g., an **a**nnoying, **b**ig cat or an **a**dventurous, **a**lley cat.

With each round, a new letter is added, e.g., an **a**nnoying, **b**ig, **c**razy cat or an **a**dventurous, **a**mber, **a**lley cat.

## ♦ GROUP DRAWING

The group is asked to form a circle.One player is given a pencil and a piece of paper. This player draws a simple drawing, like a man, a house, a tree. This player then passes it to the player on his left and this player adds to the drawing.

This same game is more exciting when each player has a piece of paper and a pencil. The players pass the papers around as before and the group drawing is finished when the papers have gone completely around the circle.

## ♦ GROUP HUG

This is easy. The whole group scrunches up and forms a tight circle with arms around each other and eyes closed.

## ♦ HUMAN PRETZEL

The group holds hands and one player is asked to turn his/her back on the group. The group then proceeds to tangle themselves up into a heap. They must do this without letting go of each others' hands. The player who turned around must now face the group and try to untangle the rest so the group is holding hands again.

## ♦ CHUCKLE BELLY

The group lies down in a single line with the second player resting their head on the first player's stomach. The third player rests their head on the second player's stomach and so on until a chain is made of all the players. Player number one now begins to laugh and the next just happens on its own. Laughter is contagious and this game proves it.

## ♦ THE CLOWN GOT SICK

The group is asked to form a circle. One player is asked to start by saying "The Clown Got Sick." The group replies, "How did he get sick?" The player responds with, "He got sick by doing this" and makes a movement, e.g., hopping up and down, winking an eye, etc. The next player on the right repeats the actions of the first and finally replies, "He got sick by doing this," and the player mimics what the first player did, which was hopping up and down, and then continues, "And from doing this," and he adds a movement of his own.

The game continues until each person has had at least one turn.

## ♦ CAR WASH

The group forms two lines. This line is the car-washing line. Players walk between the lines one at a time and the car washers shine and polish the player in the middle.

# MATERIALS FOR BRIDGING ACTIVITIES

When you are on a trip with the group or even if you are around the house, keep as many of these materials on your person as you can and keep the rest close by.

Pencils, crayons, paper, inflatable ball, ball and jacks set, deck of cards, small jack knife, ball of string, yo-yo, harmonica, finger puppets, matchbox car, and three good jokes.

CHAPTER EIGHT

# GAMES FOR THE DEVELOPING GROUP

This chapter focuses on the pragmatic use of games and activities in group development. It provides a series of games and activities for the child and youth care professional to introduce to groups at various levels of group development. Groups need to develop and to mature at their own pace and certain activities can be threatening or counter productive if introduced too early in the group's developmental process. Groups begin as a collection of individuals and if allowed to progress under controlled circumstances and with the guidance of professionally trained facilitators, they quickly develop into harmonious cooperative units.

The following series of activities is meant to take the newly formed group through a collection of group experiences that will provide them with opportunities to grow and to develop. They can, however, be utilized for groups that are already in various phases of development. They are a series of groups and follow normal group developmental phases. The initial phase of getting to know one another is important for the development of trust and should always be the primary consideration of group leaders who wish to develop a cohesive group unit. The second phase is one of experimentation with one another and can be augmented with active cooperative games. The third phase challenges the group to make decisions and to problem solve using consensus as their ideal. The final phase asks group members to trust each other to care for and treat one another with respect. When this level of development has been reached the group is truly a cohesive unit.

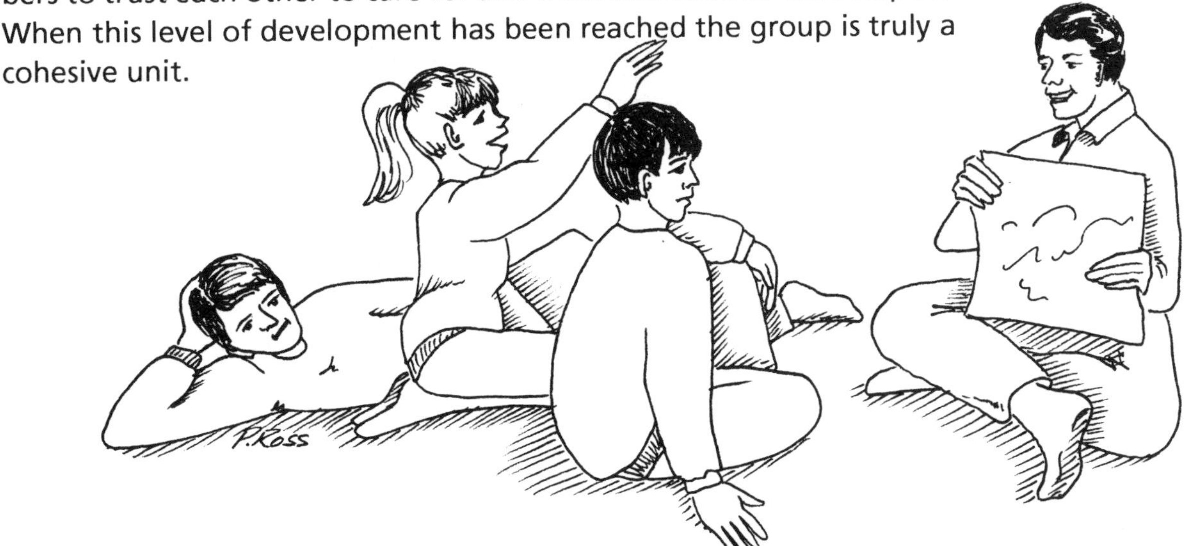

## Group Activities

### ♦ WHO'S ON MY BACK

Even before children are formally introduced to one another, they can interact in this humorous and non-threatening activity.

Cut out pictures of characters who are well known to the group members; for example, cartoon characters, movie stars, famous people, and famous places. Paste these pictures on a background of construction paper. If time is a factor and the children can read, the names can be printed on a piece of construction paper. The activity requires a character for each participant, and a safety pin so that the picture can be pinned on the back of each child's shirt.

As each member enters the room, the picture or name of the famous character is pinned on the back of their shirt. The participant is then told that they may only ask questions which require yes or no answers. Their task is to try and figure out who the character is. The participant is also instructed to answer questions from other group members with a yes or no. All players remain active until the last character is guessed.

This activity does not work well with preschoolers. Take care when selecting the characters so that the group members know who they are, and will be able to guess them fairly easily. If you are playing this game with a group who already has rapport with one another, you can increase the amount of interaction by choosing more obscure characters, or by allowing only one question for each group member.

### ♦ I AM . . . THIS IS

Names are very important when developing rapport and building self-esteem. Also, knowing someone's name makes interactions with that person more comfortable. This exercise gives the children an opportunity to hear the names of the group members. The variations of this game may give the group leader some insights into the children's interests, feelings, and self images. This works well as an opening exercise.

Call the group together and ask them to form a circle. Explain to them that you are going to play a game so the group can learn each other's names. Start with the person on your left; that person is to say "I am Bill." The person on Bill's left is to say "I am Ann, and this is Bill." The person on Ann's left is to say "I am Mary, this is Ann, and this is Bill." This process continues until the last person (you, the group leader) repeats everyone's name. "I am (group leader's name) and this is Joe, Carol, Carl, etc.", pointing to each group member as the name is said, until the whole group has been named. You might repeat the game going in the opposite direction.

**Variations:**

1) Use the same format as above, only have group members introduce themselves and add something that they enjoy doing, e.g., "I am baseball-playing Ann, and this is bike-riding Bill."
2) Use the same format as above and, this time, group members introduce themselves by describing how they feel, e.g., "I am angry Ann, and this is happy Bill."

This can be a difficult game for young children or for children with memory problems; therefore, smaller groups may need to be formed. Another way to overcome the problem of too many names to remember is to divide the circle into quarters, and to play the game with only one quarter of the names at a time. The rest of the group listens, and learns the names as well. If a group member has trouble remembering, give the person sufficient time to remember; otherwise, clues or simply miming the name can be provided by other group members. In the variations, some children may have difficulty thinking of an appropriate adjective. Before starting the activity, children can be provided with a variety of examples to help them make a selection. Provide all the support needed for this activity in order to have fun.

## ♦ I'D LIKE YOU TO MEET MY FRIEND

This exercise is a pairing exercise, and it provides the group members with their first opportunity to communicate on a one-to-one basis. It also allows the group to learn more about each of its members on a personal level.

Call the group together and ask them to pick a partner, someone whom they don't know very well. Tell the group that they have five minutes to talk to their partner in order to find out as much about them as they can (e.g., age, grade, number in family, pets, hobbies, etc.). Suggest that they take turns, and tell them that you will signal them after two and a half minutes. After the five minutes are up, ask the group to form a circle; then ask the group, one by one, to introduce their partner to the group and to include some of the information that they just received.

This is often the children's first time speaking in the group, and it can be difficult for them to remember. During the introduction to the group, allow partners to confer with one another in order to ensure that the information is correct and complete. As each member finishes, ask the partner if there is anything to add to what has been said. When each dyad has been completed, thank both members for sharing with the group.

## ♦ MIRRORING

This non-verbal exercise allows children to communicate and to begin to appreciate each other at an emotional level. The variation encourages the children to develop instant rapport.

Instruct the group to form dyads. Ask each pair to decide who will be A and who will be B. Player A is to take on a series of three poses. After each pose, player B is to imitate it. When all three poses have been mimed, player B takes on a series of three poses. Next A is asked to take on three poses that depict three different emotions. After each pose, B is to take on the pose, and guess which emotion it is depicting. Player B then takes a turn with three emotions. A is asked to take on each pose and guess which emotion it represents.

**Variations:** This exercise can be a lot of fun. If it seems appropriate at the end, each pair can discuss their experience; this can be done in the dyad or as a group discussion.

## ♦ FIND YOUR PARTNER

Making contact with members of the group, and forming connections with one another, is important to a newly formed group. In this game, children are provided with an opportunity to make these very important initial contacts.

Before conducting the activity, puzzles will be created out of construction paper or out of pictures from a magazine. Puzzles are made by cutting the construction paper or picture in a haphazard way to form two pieces. Each puzzle will require two people to solve it. Mix puzzle pieces together and ask group members to pair up with the person in the group who has the other piece of the puzzle. The game can be played several times, or can be used as a way to form dyads out of the group. Puzzles can be used to form triads or small groups by increasing the number of pieces.

## ♦ SPECIAL SOUNDS

This is a fun activity which can be useful to begin a longer pairing exercise. Children can use their imaginations to come up with their own unique sound. The variation can be used as a creative way to form dyads, triads, or small groupings.

Ask the group to pair up with someone they do not normally pair up with. Have each pair decide on a sound that they will use to identify each other. Spread the pairs around the room and ask them to close their eyes and locate their partner using only their sound to identify each other.

**Variations:** On small strips of paper, print the names of farmyard animals. Each animal will be represented by two strips of paper with their names on it. The papers are passed out, one to each participant. Children are told to read the name on the paper silently to themselves. They are not to tell anyone what their animal is. Ask the group members to spread out around the room. Instruct them to close their eyes and make the sound of their animal. When they hear another animal sound that is the same as their own, the participants are told to try to make their way around the room with the purpose of pairing up with the person making the same animal sound. This exercise can be used for forming groups of any number of individuals.

## ♦ NOTICING OTHERS

This game of observation allows group members to make more contact in a non-verbal fashion. Children are given the opportunity to observe each other at close range.

Ask the group members to pair up. If the number is uneven, one pair can form a triad. Instruct the pairs to spend two minutes noticing what their partners are wearing, the way they are sitting, and everything about them. Suggest to them that this game challenges their visual memory. When the two minutes have elapsed, ask the pairs to sit back to back. Instruct each player to change three things about themselves, e.g., remove a piece of clothing or jewelry, undo a button, roll down a sock, etc. When each player has completed this task, they are asked to turn around and face one another. Now they are to guess which three things are different.

## ♦ FAVORITES

This is another good "getting to know you" exercise. It allows children to fantasize and to exercise their visual imagery. This exercise can be presented at several different levels of complexity, from listing their favorite items, to exploring the symbolism behind the child's choice in each category.

This list can be added to, or subtracted from, in order to make it more meaningful. It can be written down, or be responded to orally.

**Procedure:** Ask the children to fill in the blanks.

My favorite food is ________ because ________ .
My favorite drink is ________ because ________ .
My favorite shape is ________ because ________ .
My favorite colour is ________ because ________ .
My favorite animal is ________ because ________ .

My favorite bird is ________ because ________ .
My favorite automobile is ________ because ________ .
My favorite toy/possession is ________ because ________ .
My favorite story/fairy tale is ________ because ________ .
My favorite dinosaur is ________ because ________ .
My favorite musical instrument is ________ because ________ .
My favorite movie/television show is ________ because ________ .
My favorite cartoon is ________ because ________ .
My favorite game/sport is ________ because ________ .
My favorite song is ________ because ________ .
My favorite hero/star/famous person is ________ because ________ .
My favorite musical group is ________ because ________.
My favorite subject in school is ________ because ________ .
My favorite friend is ________ because ________ .
My favorite relative is ________ because ________ .
My favorite character trait in others is ________ because ________ .
My favorite character trait in myself is ________ because ________ .
My favorite physical characteristic is ________ because ________ .

**Variations:** Any one or all of these favorites can be drawn or sketched to make the discussion and the experience more meaningful.

## ♦ SEVEN-UP

This is a good activity for newly formed groups and well-established groups alike. It reinforces the first names of group members, and allows for casual, non-threatening competition.

This game calls for seven players who are "It." The players stand in front of, and facing, the group. If the group is less than fifteen, it is beneficial to lessen the number of children designated as "It" in the game. All other players are to close their eyes until they are told to open them. Each of the seven players will have been instructed to quietly walk up to players who have their eyes closed, and gently tap them on the head. Note: Sometimes the tap on the head is too disruptive, and children are asked to hold their hands out so that players can touch their hands instead of their heads. Once each person has tagged a member who is not "It," and is standing back up at the front, the children are asked to open their eyes. Those who were touched are asked to stand up one by one and with one chance to guess who touched them. Players who guess correctly get to be "It," and those who guessed incorrectly can have a second turn after each player has guessed once. Older children are usually satisfied with one guess.

## ♦ GUESS WHO?

This activity provides an opportunity for group members to share a bit more information about themselves. This activity is a good guessing game, and it encourages the improvement of memory skills.

Pass out paper and pencils, and instruct group members to write down three things about themselves that the other group members may not know, for example, middle names, hobbies, places visited, secret ambitions, etc. Instruct the group members to keep their answers confidential, to write them down on the paper provided, to fold the paper, and to place it on the table. When all papers are handed in, mix up the papers and read them to the group one at a time. Each member of the group is given a turn to guess who the author is, until someone guesses correctly. If they are unable to guess, the paper goes back into the pile. The activity is completed when all the players have been guessed.

## ♦ DIFFERENCES

This activity allows group members to share some personal information in a small group setting. It asks the group members to begin to cooperate with each other and to share resources. It is another step closer towards forming a healthy and constructive group.

If the group has over eight members, divide it into smaller groups of four to six children. Each small group is given a pencil, tape measure, and set of bathroom scales. When the groups are formed, present each group member with the following list:

a) What is your full name?
b) What day, month, and year were you born?
c) What city/town were you born in?
d) How tall are you?
e) How much do you weigh?
f) What is the color of your eyes?
g) What is the color of your hair?
h) What is your ancestry?
i) Do you belong to a specific religious group?
j) Who is your best friend?
k) How many people are in your family and what are their names?

Ask each of the group members to gather the information requested and to write it down on the sheet provided. When lists are completed, information can be shared with the small group and then with the entire group if time allows. It should be mentioned that group cooperation is necessary for the activity to be fully enjoyed.

**Variations:** Present the following list to each member of each grouping:

a) What is your favorite subject in school?
b) List two activities you do well.
c) What is the name of a book that you enjoyed?
d) List places you have visited.
e) Name two things that scare you.

Ask the group members to gather information and to try not to be influenced by other answers. Once the lists are complete, they can be shared with the entire group. This can be followed by a discussion about how differences can become resources in a positive group setting. The information gathered now becomes a list of combined talents and group resources.

## ♦ PERSONAL SPACE

An excellent way to help group members is to define personal space before continuing on to more challenging forms of group interactions. When the results are shared in the group, members have a good understanding of each other's limits.

Ask the group members to form pairs. Request that one member of the pair be A and the other be B. A is to stand in front of B, approximately six feet away. When B is ready, A is to slowly walk toward B, and must stop when B signals him to stop. B is to stop A when they are as close as B would like that person to come. Repeat this procedure with A standing on B's left, right, and back. Repeat the whole exercise with A and B switching places.

Discuss with the group, in terms of how each group member felt and where their boundaries were. Focus questions might be: Do your boundaries vary with different people? Is it important to respect people's personal space?

## ♦ CONTACT EXERCISE

This exercise allows group members to gradually begin to make contact with each other. If it is done in a fun-loving, non-threatening way, it allows group members to slowly enter into each other's personal space.

Ask the group members to begin walking around the room helter skelter with their eyes down, noticing no one but themselves. After a few minutes, ask the group to continue moving, but to make eye contact with each group member. No talking is allowed. In time, ask them to move faster, but to avoid bumping. Next, ask them to slow down and then to speed up. When the group seems to be warming up, ask them to continue moving slowly, and to shake hands with each other without talking. Shake left hands, elbows, knees, bums, backs, feet, etc.

## ♦ GRANDMOTHER'S TRUNK

This is a good circle activity that exercises the memory and sequencing abilities. The variation serves as another reminder for names, and assists the memory process by word association.

Ask the group to form a circle. Tell the group that you want them all to think of something to put into Grandmother's trunk. Appoint someone to go first. This player begins by saying, "I put a *teapot* in Grandmother's trunk." The next repeats the statement and adds their item, e.g., "I put a teapot and an *elephant* in Grandmother's trunk." Each player in turn repeats the objects already in the trunk, and then adds another to the growing list.

**Variations:** Use the same format. Player begins by saying their name and they must think of an item to put in the trunk that begins with the same letter as their first name, e.g., "My name is Mike and I put a *melon* in Grandmother's trunk." The next player, Bob, would say "Mike put in a melon. My name is Bob and I put in a bat." The next player, Joe, would say, "Mike put in a melon, Bob put in a bat. My name is Joe and I put in a joke." This would continue around the circle until all had finished.

If the players have difficulty remembering, allow them extra time, or they may ask someone in the group for help.

## ♦ CATEGORIES

This is a good game that promotes group cooperation and sameness. The rhythm in the game, as well as its non-competitive nature, allows the group to have fun with cooperation.

Ask the players to sit or stand in a circle and appoint someone to go first. This player thinks up a category such as animals, countries, colors, etc. Once the category has been chosen, that person is ready to start the beat. The beat is marked out by first slapping with hands on knees, then clapping with hands together, then snapping the fingers on one hand, then the other hand. The rhythm goes slap, clap, snap, snap, slap, clap, snap, snap, and so on. The leader chants. Let's play (slap) categories (clap) such as (snap) *animals* (snap). Keeping in time, the next player must chime in with the name of an animal, for example (slap), (clap), (snap), *tiger*, (snap), (slap), (clap), (snap), *elephant*, (snap), and so on around the circle. As the group gets the hang of categories, speed up the pace until the group bursts into laughter.

It is best to start this game at a slow speed. If the slap, clap, snap, snap rhythm is too difficult, children can merely clap in time.

## ♦ CATERPILLAR RACE

This is a lively game that relies on team work and the cooperation of group members. This game may take two or three sessions to master. It can become a favorite, and one that gets played quite often.

Divide the group into small teams. Instruct the teams to squat down, one behind the other, and to put their arms around each other's waist. Each team is then to practice moving up and down in unison. Once they have mastered this skill, have them hop forward together. Suggest that counting, "one, two, three, hop" may help the team to time the jump. After the teams have developed skills in moving forward, line the teams up and have a chase. The front of one caterpillar must tag the rear of another caterpillar.

## ♦ PEOPLE PACKAGES

This is another game that is enjoyable and non-threatening. Group decisions are important, and the dynamics of how particular groups make decisions can be enlightening for all.

**Materials:** Newspaper, wrapping paper, string, scotch or masking tape, and any other types of packaging materials.

Divide the group into two teams of four or five members. Instruct the teams to decide on one member to be the package. Tell the teams to begin to wrap their surprise packages when you give the signal. When the packages are completed, or when the time limit is up, encourage members to look around at the other packages and to comment on their handiwork.

## ♦ CREATIVE BLOCK BUILDING

Sometimes language and how it is interpreted can hamper relationships. This interesting activity stresses the importance of clear and detailed instructions.

**Materials:** Sets of wooden blocks; each set should have no less than eight identical pairs of blocks.

Instruct the group to form a circle. Ask for two volunteers and request them to sit back to back in the middle of the circle. Give each volunteer a set of blocks. Appoint one volunteer to be A and one to be B. A is to build a structure with the blocks, and to give B the necessary instructions in order to build an identical structure. Neither A or B is allowed to turn around, and only A may speak (for young children and those experiencing difficulties, allow dialogues between A and B). Discuss with the children how instructing can be misunderstood. Discuss how clear communication adds to better understanding.

## ♦ COOPERATION

This is an excellent activity to study and teach group dynamics. Cooperation is essential for the group to succeed in this activity and strategies for cooperation can be discussed. An observer and rule keeper can be assigned to each group of five in order to make the discussion more fruitful.

Prepare a set of five squares as shown in the illustration for each group, cutting each square in three as shown. Mix up the pieces so that you have five piles of three pieces, each one in no way a match for the other. Place each pile into an envelope. Outline the following rules to each group.

The group's task is to form five small squares using the pieces in these five envelopes. The pieces in each of the envelopes will not form a square by themselves; therefore, individual cooperation and that of the group is necessary to complete this exercise.

Each individual is given an envelope. Once the envelopes are passed out there is to be no talking until the task is completed. Gestures and any other form of direction are not allowed.

The task for each member is to form a square from the shapes in their envelope. Cooperation is underscored through the individual's ability to observe and to exchange the required pieces without gesturing.

Participants may give up pieces to other members but they may not take pieces from others.

Participants may not put their pieces in the center for others to pick up. Pieces may only be given to individual members.

Pass out the envelopes and watch the fun begin. Give them fifteen to twenty minutes to complete.

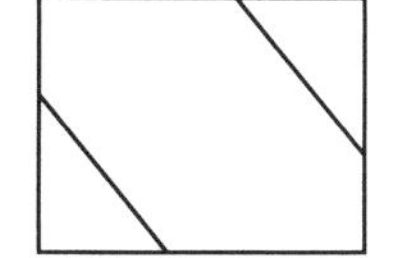 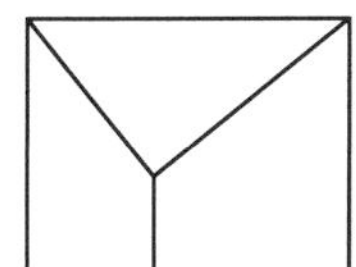 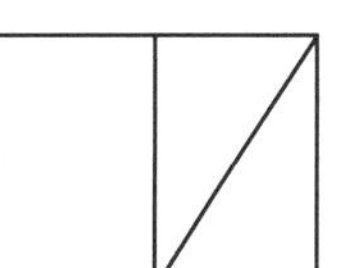 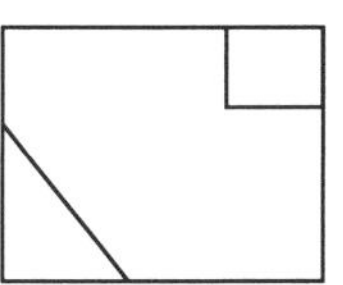 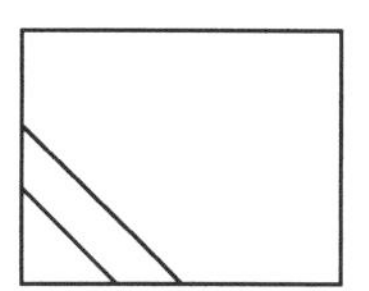

## ♦ THE VOYAGE

This is a good activity to allow the group to use its creativity. There is very little structure which allows the children to control, to cooperate, to withdraw, or to do whatever they feel. "Leadership" and group roles are evident in the interactions. It might take props and some enthusiasm to help the more inhibited children to feel comfortable; however, the art of running these types of activities is to conclude them to everyone's satisfaction.

Ask the group to fantasize a trip to a lost continent or to outer space. Instruct them to lie down and to relax in order to help them to fantasize the voyage. Have them ad-lib a journey to either of the above. When the group seems to be well into it, suggest that you are going to ask them to get up and to interact with each other as if they had just arrived, and that their mission is to survive long enough until they are joined by their allies, i.e., they will need food, shelter, etc., to exist which will form a basis for the interactions.

Allow twenty minutes to one hour, depending on group involvement, for the drama to be played out.

## ♦ SURVIVAL

This activity can provide the group leader with a wealth of knowledge in terms of the particular dynamics of the group. A good time to present such an activity would be when the adult group leader feels that the level of comfort in the group is sufficient to warrant their handling of this sometimes very frustrating exercise. A role play or re-enactment of an actual situation makes this activity more exciting.

**Materials:** Paper and pencils. I have found, with younger children, that it helps if you have pictures or objects to represent the items available to take on the raft.

Divide the children into groups of eight and ask the children to imagine that they are on a boat that is sinking in the middle of the ocean. Each group has a life raft which is big enough to hold all of them, and enough room for six other items. Their task is to choose which six items they will take from the following list. Instruct the individual members to go through the exercise alone first, and to prioritize the items they would choose in order of importance:

- Purification tablets for drinking water (8 tablets)
- Food (enough for three days)
- Puppy

- Motor for raft
- Gas for motor (12-gallon tank)
- Paddles (2)
- Fishing rod and hooks
- Life jackets (6)
- One woollen blanket
- Waterproof matches
- Compass
- Water jug
- Swiss Army Knife (pocket knife with several attachments)

After each child has numbered the items in order of importance, instruct them to join their small groups. The task of the group is to collectively agree on six items to take with them in the time allotted. When appropriate, the group should be signalled when five minutes of the time allotted remains, and when one minute is left before conclusion.

The children should be given the opportunity to express their feelings concerning the exercise.

This exercise can be lengthy and it would be best for the group leader to place time limits on the group. Consensus in decision making is necessary and this should be explained to the group members before they start the group exercise.

## ♦ LETTING GO

This exercise requires a certain level of trust among group members; therefore, take some time beforehand to decide on dyads that will work well together.

When the dyads have been assigned, one partner lies down and slowly relaxes. When relaxed, that person will allow the partner to lift up his/her arm and to move it without needing to control the movement of the arm; it is totally limp. Repeat this procedure for the other arm and the two legs. If the partners are really trusting, they can allow each other to gently cradle their head in their two hands, gently rocking it back and forth.

## ♦ TRUSTING

This exercise also requires a healthy degree of trust among group members. Discuss with the group the seriousness of the risk involved.

Divide the group up into triads and have the triad decide who will be A, B, and C. A begins and stands with his/her back to B and C.

When A is ready, A is to fall forward into B's outstretched hands, B, in turn, supports A and gently propels A backward into C's outstretched hands. B and C push A forward and backward gently. B and C can start out standing close together and then slowly move back to a safe distance as A's trust in them increases. A decides when they move and how far back they move.

Now B takes a turn with A and C to catch and finally C takes a turn.

## ♦ TRUST WALK

Once again trust and maturity is a must for this exercise.

Divide the group into pairs and give each pair a blindfold. The pair decides who will be blindfolded first. The guide will stand close to the person blindfolded and will hold on to this person or keep in touch physically with the blindfolded person at all times. The guide then leads the blindfolded person on a discovery journey. The guide points out various aspects of the environment and encourages the blindfolded person to experience it without eyes.

## ♦ TRUST GUIDE

This is an excellent exercise to finish off an activity program. Group members are literally supported by one another.

Ask the group to form a very tight circle. Members of the group take turns volunteering to stand in the middle of the circle. The person in the middle closes his/her eyes and allows him/herself to fall forward and backward supported by the hands of the group. The person in the middle is gently passed around the circle until the time is up or if that person decides to stop earlier.

## ♦ ROCK THE BABY

Here is another excellent way to complete a program. This is a very powerful exercise; a healthy attitude and gentle nature is necessary.

Divide the group into two lines and have the lines facing one another. One group member at a time volunteers to lie down between the first six pairs of players and closes his/her eyes. The group of twelve squat down and gently place their hands underneath the body of the lying person. On the count of three, the group slowly lifts the group member until all twelve are standing. The group gently rocks the person to and fro; if it is a large group, they gently pass the person down the line to the next twelve and so on.

CHAPTER NINE

# LEADER AND LEADERLESS GAMES

This chapter focuses on leadership in the group. Its aim is to develop the individual group member's ability to lead and for the group as a collective to feel comfortable with each member taking on a leadership role. The leaderless games are designed to allow the group to function as a unit without the need to have one person as a director.

The games and activities are designed to allow for various degrees of competition within the group. The first series of activities are leaderless and have little or no competitive elements in them. The next level of games offers competitive experiences but does not fall into the win-lose category. The final level involves team games where one team is in competition with the other.

Child and youth care professionals are cautioned to introduce competitive games into their curriculum only when they feel that this will not disrupt cohesiveness within the group as a whole. It is far better to leave the team-competitive activities to the later stages of the group's development. Various techniques can be utilized to make the team activities less competitive in order to make them more enjoyable for the whole group.

## Group Activities

### ♦ THIS IS THE HOUSE THAT JACK BUILT

One player begins with "This is the house that Jack built" and the next player adds on to the line, "This is the Ferrari that is parked on the street in front of the house that Jack built." The next player adds on, "This is the driver that sits in the Ferrari in front of the house that Jack built." The game continues until all of the players have had a turn.

### ♦ FACE FLASHING

The group sits in a circle; players decide on the weirdest-looking face they could make. Player number one starts the game by turning to the player on the left and making a weird face. This player reacts to player number one's face by making a face. This player, player number two, turns to the player on the left and mimics player number one's face. Player number three reacts to the face and turns to the left and mimics player number one's face. This continues around the circle until player number one's weird face has come full-circle. Now it's player number two's turn to make a face and have it mimicked by all the players as before. The group plays until each person has had a turn.

### ♦ ONE THOUSAND WORDS

Cut out some provocative pictures from various magazines and show them to the group, one by one. Ask group members in turn to respond as if they were one or all of the characters in the picture.

### ♦ TEN SECOND LOOK

Ask the group to form a circle. Hand out sheets of paper and pencils to each group member. One player begins by secretly drawing a simple sketch of a house, a tree, a person, etc., so that no one can see what they have drawn. The artist then allows the group member on the left to sneak a peek at the drawing for the count of ten. This player then in turn draws what s/he saw secretly so that no one can see. This artist in turn allows the player on the left to see the drawing for ten seconds. This player repeats the procedure until the drawing has gone completely around the room.

The originator of the drawing compares his/her drawing with the drawings of the other artists. The more complex the original drawing, the more distorted the final drawing.

## ♦ SCULPTING STATUES

Ask the group to form triads and identify each other as A, B, or C. A is to be the sculptor, B is to be the model, and C is to be the clay. B and C are asked to stand close to each other, allowing enough room for A to move in between them. A, with closed eyes, is to be positioned facing B and C. B is to take on a pose, the more bizarre the better. Just by using the sense of touch, A is to manipulate C into a similar pose.

## ♦ GROUP PULL-UPS

Divide the group into pairs and ask each member to sit back to back on the ground. When they are ready, each pair is to stand up as one unit while remaining back to back. When they have completed this task they are to assist whoever needs help until the whole group is standing. Now divide the group into threes and then fours until the whole group is sitting back to back. The final stand is the group pull-up.

## ♦ BALANCE AND SUPPORT

Divide the group into pairs according to height. Instruct the pairs to face each other and to stand with their palms facing out and their arms extended. The partners slowly walk backward with their weight supported by their outstretched hands. The pair continues until it has formed a two-human triangle. When the pair has been successful, they are to join another twosome to form a four-pod balancing structure. The group continues until all group members are standing in a tight circle supported by each other's hands.

## ♦ BODY ROLLING

Instruct the group members to lie down on the ground beside one another in a continuous line. Choose one person and instruct him/her to lie face down across the line of bodies. Now, instruct the line of bodies to roll.

This rolling propels the person on top right down to the end of the line. The person gets off and lies down with the group and the player at the beginning of the line stands up and lies across the bodies for a ride.

## ♦ CONVEYOR BELT

Instruct the group to form a single line behind one another. Player one is asked to take one-half turn left and player two is asked to take one-half turn right. This continues down the line so that players are facing alternate directions. Now ask players to sit and eventually lie down in the same order. Each member is now lying on his/her back, shoulder to shoulder with the next person still facing the opposite or alternate direction.

Players are instructed to hold out their hands with palms facing upwards. These outstretched hands are the conveyor belt. A player is selected beforehand to be the product on the conveyor belt; this person then lies face up on the conveyor belt. The conveyer belt (outstretched hands) propels the product by supporting and moving the player along.

## ♦ STORMY WEATHER

The leader instructs the group to sit in a circle. The leader begins by rubbing his/her hands together to make a swishing sound. The person to the left of the leader imitates the leader and now both of them are rubbing their hands together to make swishing sounds.

The next player to the left starts to rub his/her hands together and so on around the circle. Once the group has done this action they are to practice until they can make the swishing sound start with the leader and travel around the circle back to the leader again. The group can experiment by making the sound travel to the left and to the right. The leader then suggests that the swishing sound will represent the sound of the rain.

The leader then repeats the above exercise only replacing the action of rubbing hands to clapping the hands. The leader suggests that the hand clapping sound can represent the thunder.

The exercise is repeated again using finger snapping to represent lightning and again using thigh slapping to represent heavy rainfall.

Once the group has become proficient at making all the sounds, travel around the circle. The leader begins with raindrops that get progressively faster and louder as they go around the circle. Each player must watch closely and imitate exactly what s/he sees the person on the right is doing. The leader experiments with the sounds to create the illusion of a thunder storm. When the level of skill with this exercise increases, members can take a turn at creating their own storms.

## ♦ GAME SHOW

Each child is to think of a favourite game, activity, stunt, skit, etc. It must be one that takes less than ten minutes to play and one that can be easily taught to the group. Children are also allowed to make up their own version of a popular game.

## ♦ BACK TO BACK

Ask the group to choose a partner and to stand facing one another. The person who does not have a partner is then designated as the leader. The leader calls out commands, e.g., touch hands to hands, touch feet to feet, touch back to back. When the leader calls out "Switch," everyone is to find a new partner, including the leader. The person who is left now becomes the new leader. The game continues like this until the allotted time has elapsed.

## ♦ ZIT AND DOUBLE ZIT

Ask the players to form a circle. Appoint one player to be "It" and ask them to stand in the middle. Ask the person who is "It" to choose two categories, e.g., food and colors. The first category is called ZIT and the second category is called ZIT ZIT, i.e., a food name is ZIT and a name of a color is a ZIT ZIT. Instruct "It" to begin to name something and point to a player in the circle. After each word, "It" is to count softly to five to allow the person time to answer. As "It" names things, the person who is pointed to must answer either ZIT, ZIT ZIT, or remain silent. Using the example of food and colors, if a food was named, the appropriate reply would be ZIT, if a color was named, the reply would be ZIT ZIT, if the thing named was neither food nor color, the player is to remain silent. If the player replies correctly, the game continues. If the player gives the incorrect reply, they are asked to be "It" and to choose two new categories.

## ♦ HEADS AND HIPS

Have the players sit in a circle and appoint a leader to stand in the middle of the circle. Instruct the leader to spin around and to point to someone in the group with one hand and to put the other hand on his/her head or hip. If the leader puts a hand on the head, the person pointed to must say his/her own first name. If the leader puts his/her hand on the hip, the person pointed to must say his/her own last name. The leader is allowed to have as many turns as there are players and then must choose someone else to take the role as leader.

## ♦ LEADER

Ask the group to form a circle. This game can be played sitting or standing. One member steps out and turns away from the circle. Then the group leader touches someone, or points to someone, and that person becomes the "Leader." The group is to imitate whatever action the leader makes, e.g., claps hands or scratches forehead. The leader decides what the group will do, and when they will change. Once the leader has been appointed, it is up to the person who was outside the circle to come back and to guess who the leader is. Four guesses are allowed. If that person is successful, then the "leader" becomes the next person who guesses in the new game. If unsuccessful, then that person must choose someone to leave the circle who will then attempt to guess the new leader. The new leader will be appointed in the same way as in the beginning of the game.

## ♦ FRENCH BLIND MAN'S BLUFF

Form a circle with the group and ask for a volunteer to be the blind man. Blindfold the volunteer, and hand him/her the stick. Place the blind man in the center. Instruct the group to join hands and to move around the blind man. Tell the blind man to tap his/her stick on the floor, and when the tapping stops, the group is to stop moving. Once the group has stopped, the blind man points his/her stick towards a member of the group. The member who is pointed to must say "Blind man, blind man, guess who I am." If the blind man guesses correctly, that person continues as the blind man. If the blind man guesses incorrectly then s/he must appoint someone else to be the blind man.

## ♦ AIR, EARTH AND WATER

Ask the group to form a circle and to appoint someone to go first. Instruct this player to turn to the person on the left and say either "earth, air, or water." The person on the left must then name an animal that lives on land if it is earth; name a fish or water animal if it is water; name a bird if it is air. If the player is unable to answer or answers incorrectly the person on the left may attempt to answer. If the player answers correctly, that person can turn to the person on the left and say either, "earth, air, or water."

## ♦ TOUCH AND TELL

Ask the group to form a circle. Choose one player to come into the center to be blindfolded. The rest of the players are then told to walk around the circle to the right, and then they are signalled to stop. The blindfolded player is then told to walk forward with arms outstretched until s/he touches somebody. The player continues to touch the person until he/she can guess who it is, and if guessed correctly, that person may go again. If the guess is incorrect, the person that was touched becomes "It."

## ♦ DOG IN THE MANGER

Draw a circle on the floor with the chalk, approximately four feet in diameter (this is to be the manger). Ask for a volunteer to be the dog. Instruct the rest of the group to form a larger circle around the manger.

Inside the small circle, place one of the items, e.g., pine cones, sticks, pebbles, etc. The object of the game is for one of the group members to snatch the item from the manger without the dog touching that person. More than one person may sneak up on the dog; however, only one person at a time can snatch an item out of the manger. If the dog touches that person before s/he is out of the circle, that person must go back to his/her place. The person who successfully snatches the item out of the manger without being touched becomes the dog and a new turn begins.

## ♦ RHYMING RIDDLE GAME

Ask the group to form a circle. Appoint one member to start. The first player asks the member on the right to solve a rhyming riddle, e.g., "I'm thinking of a (pet) that rhymes with (log)." Answer: dog. "I'm thinking of something that's found in the (kitchen) and it rhymes with (pink)." Answer: sink. The player must solve the riddle on their first guess. If not, the person to the right has a chance to guess the riddle. When the riddle is solved, the player solving the riddle now becomes the riddler.

## ♦ SPUD

Ask the group to make a tight circle around a ball (which is placed on the ground). One person is chosen as "It" and stands in the middle of the circle and throws the ball high into the air, calling out the name of one of the members of the group. The rest of the group members try to run as far away from the ball as possible. Whoever is named, runs for the ball, and when that person has it, s/he is to yell out "SPUD." When the player yells "SPUD" all must freeze in their tracks.

The caller is then allowed to take four steps in any direction. Then s/he is to throw the ball at one of the players. If the ball misses, the thrower gets an "S." If the player is hit, then that player gets the "S." This continues until each member gets S-P-U-D. The group regathers after each shot and no one is eliminated. Whoever gets the letter is the new caller and can call out any name.

## ♦ DROP THE HANDKERCHIEF

Ask the group to form a circle. Someone is chosen as "It." Players are either standing or sitting. "It" walks around the outside of the circle. At some point, "It" drops the handkerchief behind one of the players. Once the player realizes the handkerchief was dropped, s/he must chase "It" and tag him/her before "It" reaches the chaser's spot in the circle. If the chaser is successful in catching "It" before s/he reaches his/her place, then the person who was "It" must try again to give away the hankerchief. If the chaser is unsuccessful then s/he becomes "It."

This game can be played while singing a song and using an envelope while the person who is "It" walks around the circle:

I wrote a letter to my love
And on the way I dropped it.
A little doggie picked it up
And put it in his pocket.
He won't bite you and won't bite me
But he'll bite the one who's got it.
So hurry up and drop it.

## ♦ DEAD MAN

Ask the group to lie down and to have enough space around them so that they are not touching each other. Pick the person who seems the most relaxed to be "It." Members are asked to be as still as possible; if they move and the person who is "It" sees them, then they are "It" as well. The game proceeds until one member is left lying.

## ♦ RED ROVER, RED ROVER

Choose two captains. Ask them to pick teams. The teams face each other at a distance of about twenty feet; instruct them to lock hands, wrists, or arms in order to form a human chain. Starting with the first team, a player from that team calls upon a player of the opposite team in this way:

"Red Rover, Red Rover, please send someone over
Red Rover, Red Rover, send (person's name) over."

The person whose name was called runs toward the opposite chain in an attempt to break the chain. If the runner manages to break the chain, that person returns to his/her team, bringing one of the players from the opposite team along (they choose which player they will bring). If the runner is unsuccessful at breaking the chain s/he is captured and becomes a member of the other team. Eventually, one team is down to one member and the game ends.

## ♦ RATTLESNAKE TAG

Appoint two leaders. Ask them to choose two teams. Each team forms a line or snake behind its leader. Players attach themselves to the teammate in front of them by putting their hands on the shoulders or waist of that player. Both teams must begin side by side and facing in the same direction, with the leaders at the front of the line. On the word "Go," the leader of each team must try to touch the last person in line or the tail of the opposite team. The first leader to tag wins. If the chain breaks, the leader must tag the last player linked up with the opposite team leader.

## ♦ HAWKS AND DOVES

Randomly divide the group up into two groups or four groups depending upon group size. One group is called the hawks, who are violent and aggressive by nature. The second group is called the doves, who are non-violent and passive by nature. Divide the room in half in some way so that the hawks or doves are not allowed to cross over to one another's side or space. Give the hawks and doves a problem to discuss, e.g., war, discrimination, children's rights, crime, etc. The hawks can only give violent solutions. The hawks are allowed to lose their tempers. The doves must try to remain as calm as possible and give non-violent solutions to the problem. Group leaders will allow each group member to have opinions. When each group member has had a turn, then ask the sides to switch roles. The hawks becomes the doves and the doves become the hawks. Repeat the process giving each group equal time. When each group member has had a chance to speak on both topics the activity is finished.

Ask the group to write down how this experience felt for them. What emotions and internal images were present when role playing the hawk and the dove? How is the world like this game? How is the country like this game? How is the neighbourhood, classroom, or family like this game? Brainstorm for appropriate solutions to discourage violence and encourage non-violence.

CHAPTER TEN

# THE CONVALESCENT AND SPECIAL NEEDS CHILD

The vast majority of games and activities presented in this book can be adapted by creative child and youth care professionals to suit the needs of any group of children that they are working with. The games in this section are focused on the child who has very little mobility or limited mobility. These games are excellent for groups of children whose mobility is limited by their environment or those children who are limited by their physical self. When children are bedridden or confined, they are easily bored and they often resort to television or other passive forms of leisure entertainment. These passive exercises can reinforce feelings of helplessness and add to the child or youth's depression and low feelings of self-worth. When the child's mind is challenged during these periods of inactivity, the child increases feelings of competence and self-worth. When the environment can be structured to allow for some movement or exchange among the group members, the individuals have an opportunity to combat the frustrations of their confinement.

Children and youth can also react aggressively to inactivity and boredom. Lack of purpose or structure can cause feelings of insecurity and fear. Whenever possible, children and youth should be allowed to express themselves and to live in their worlds. This confinement or restraint can cause them serious depression and apathy. Quiet games, loud games, games that challenge the children to use non-physical abilities to stimulate themselves can be effective ways to overcome these problems.

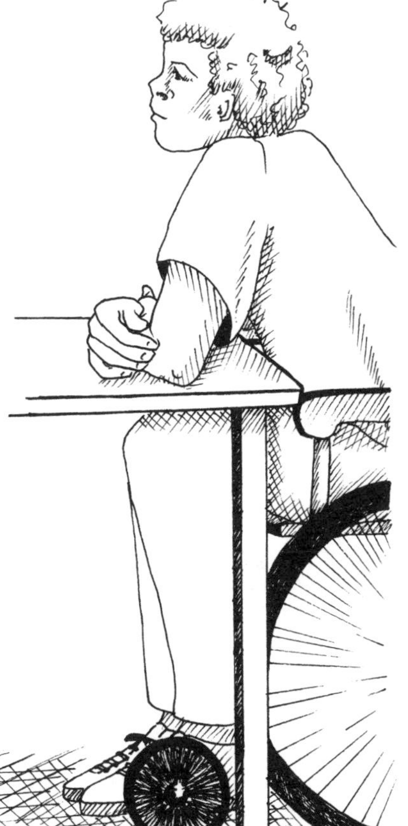

## Group and Individual Activities

### ♦ BEDSIDE BEANBAG BASKETBALL

Attach a string to a beanbag or to a small ball and attach the other end to the bed or chair. Place a pail close enough to the bed or chair so that the player can easily score a basket. The child can move the basket further away and lengthen the string as s/he gains in competence.

This game is a lot of fun between beds where the player has to be first in the basket to gain the point.

### ♦ TABOO AND GIRAFFE

Taboo is a word game that asks the players to carry on a conversation about a certain person, place or thing; however, they are not allowed to say the person's name or the name of the place or thing. They must replace the name with the word taboo.

Giraffe is a game of silence and who can stay quiet the longest. Hand signals can be used during the game of Giraffe so that the players can still communicate.

### ♦ LAUGHING FACE

This is a pencil and paper game using the name of a person, place or thing. Each player thinks of a famous person, place, or thing that everyone in the group knows about; e.g., television show, local landmark, or teacher's name.

The person who goes first indicates the number of letters and words in the name by drawing a short line to indicate a single letter and a space between the short lines to mark off one word from the other. For example, **MARTIN LUTHER KING** would be:

_ _ _ _ _ _   _ _ _ _ _ _   _ _ _ _

The group is asked to decide who this famous person is by guessing letters of the famous person's name. If a member guesses a letter and it is not in the word then a part gets added on to the laughing face.

The parts of the laughing face in order are: head, left eye, right eye, nose, mouth, left ear and right ear. When the laughing face is completed, the group gets one last guess. If they still don't guess correctly, the player may go again or pass the pencil onto the next person. If a member of the group is able to guess the name before the laughing face is completed then that person may take a turn.

## ♦ ART CHARADES

To play this game the adult leader prepares a list of movies or famous names, etc. The group is divided into teams of no less than five players for each team.

The game begins by each team sending one team member to the adult leader. The adult leader quietly tells the team representatives the movie or name. The team representatives then race back to their teams; by communicating to the team members by drawing pictures or symbols, they try to get their teams to correctly guess the movie or famous person. The first team to guess correctly and to sit down wins the game.

## ♦ HORSE, PIG, DONKEY, PENNY, BALL TOSS

This game is simple and can be played in the style of Bedside Beanbag Basketball. Each player may use a penny, ball, or object; or the group may wish to share an object. A target is established; e.g., a waste basket, a mark on the wall, a hoop, etc. Players are given letters for each successful hit on the target. The first person to spell out the words: horse, pig, or donkey is the winner.

## ♦ TIME QUIZZES

These can take many forms but the two major ideas are guessing when certain time intervals occur, e.g., clap when thirty seconds is up or guess how many times something will occur in a designated span, e.g., how many green cars will pass by in the next three minutes.

## ♦ I'M THINKING, I'VE GOT A SECRET, OR NAME THAT TUNE

I'm Thinking is a guessing game much like I Spy. "I'm thinking of an animal that rhymes with now." "I'm thinking of a person that rhymes with pill." "I'm thinking of a show that rhymes with granny."

I've Got a Secret is a guessing game where a player thinks of a famous person, place, or thing. The group can ask the person questions and s/he must answer with either a yes or no. The group must guess the secret.

Name That Tune is also a guessing game. It requires a source of music. The game starts when the first three to five seconds of the song are played. The players must guess the song title or ask a question that requires a yes or no answer; e.g., Is this a "Rock and Roll" song?

## ♦ THE LETTER GUESSING GAME

The player who starts has sixty seconds to think of as many words that start with a certain letter of the alphabet. You have to be able to find the word in the dictionary. A variation is naming things in your environment that start with a certain letter.

## ♦ DICTIONARY

This game needs at least four players and a dictionary. The first player selects an obscure word from the dictionary and says the word out loud to the rest of the group. The first player writes down the dictionary meaning of this word and the others will invent a meaning and write it down. All the meanings are collected by the person with the dictionary meaning and s/he must read them out loud. The players must then decide which one is the correct meaning.

## ♦ LEFT-HANDED, BLINDFOLDED, OR FOOT DRAWINGS

Write down the names of common objects on pieces of paper: man, woman, tree, store, car, house, etc., and place them in a bowl.

Left-Handed is a game where after the person selects an object s/he must draw his object with the left hand. The first group member to guess the object can have his turn next. The game continues until each person has had a turn.

Blindfolded is similar to Left-Handed except the player selects an object and then must draw it blindfolded.

Foot Drawings is once again similar to the others except that the artist must draw with a foot.

## ♦ CONCENTRATION

This game is played with a deck of cards. Four rows of cards, with six cards in each row are laid out with the cards face down. Players must take turns, turning over two cards on each turn to try to make a match. The card must be turned face up so that all can see. If players make a match on their turn, they can go again until they are unsuccessful at making a pair. The dealer will replace that pair with two new cards face down on the table. The game continues until all cards are matched.

## ♦ WHATCHA GOT IN THE BAG

This is a guessing game that involves a variety of common objects and a paper or a cloth bag. The player who goes first secretly places an object into the bag and then places the bag in the middle of the group. The group, by means of questions that require a yes or no answer, tries to guess what is in the bag.

## ♦ WHERE AM I? WHERE DO I WANT TO BE? WHAT IS STOPPING ME?

These are three questions that child and youth constantly ask themselves. If one is confined or bedridden, these three questions become every more critical.

Ask the group to concentrate on these three questions.

Ask the group the following questions. It may be useful to write them down or give the group materials to write them down or have long pauses after each question in order for them to reflect on their answer.

- Where am I?
- What is happening in my present life?
- What are my likes and dislikes?
- Where do I want to go?
- What are my aspirations for the future?
- Where am I going?
- What is preventing me?
- What are the challenges that await me?
- What do I have to do to attain my goals?

While the group members are pondering these questions, pass out three small sheets or one large sheet of paper and markers, pastels, or pencil crayons.

When the group has finished contemplating the last question, ask them to draw on their sheets of paper or to divide the large paper into three and to draw pictures, symbols and colors that would illustrate their thoughts on the three main questions: Where am I? Where do I want to be? What is preventing me?

## Travel Games

### ♦ EAGLE EYE

This is a game that is preplanned by someone who knows the journey well. Several landmarks that are on the route are selected, listed, and given different point values, depending on how difficult they are to see. Other more common persons, places, or things can also be included in the game and they would be given a lesser point value. The player who sees the landmark first scores the appropriate point value.

### ♦ RADAR EARS

This game is played with paper and pens about half way into the trip. Make sure the radio has been playing. Ask the group to make a list of all the songs including song writers and recording artists that have been played on the radio during the trip. They might also list the commercials and news items that have been broadcasted.

### ♦ CARTOON TRIVIA

Each player thinks of a favourite cartoon character. The player who goes first concentrates on his/her cartoon character while the rest of the group tries to guess who the cartoon character is. This player can only answer by nodding "yes" or shaking his/her head "no." The player whose cartoon character requires the most guesses wins. Each cartoon character receives one point for each question asked.

### ♦ TRAVELLING ALPHABET

Players must follow the sequence of the alphabet and locate signs that have firstly the letter A and then B, C, D and so on, until the whole alphabet is spelled out. Only one letter per sign is allowed. This can also be played by counting out 1, 2, 3, 4, 5, 6, 7, 8, 9, 0 on licence plates of cars and only one number per plate.

### ♦ SEEING, LISTENING AND COUNTING

Seeing is a game where group members challenge each other by calling "It" just after the car leaves a small town. Whoever calls "It" first, challenges the group to a certain challenge; e.g., list five objects that you saw in the last town that will fit into a milk bottle. List ten objects that were bright red. List seven buildings that were made of brick, and so on. The challenger must have a correct answer for the group as well. When the group accepts the challenge the game is on. The first player to complete his list wins.

### ♦ GRAVEYARD POKER

As you are driving along, have group members look for certain features, e.g., a red tractor, a cow, a red barn, a graveyard, etc. Assign points according to how easy or difficult it will be to see these objects. You might give 20 points (the maximum) for a graveyard and 5 points for a cow. Make a left-side and a right-side team.

### ♦ LICENSE PLATES

Everyone is on his/her own here. By taking turns, each player gets to make a word from the letters of a licence plate travelling in front of the vehicle. No place names or people's names allowed.

## CHILD AND YOUTH CARE TRAVELLING KIT

This kit will fit in a small travelling case and can be used for many different occasions. This list can be added to or subtracted from depending on the needs of the group.

- Clipboards, pieces of heavy cardboard, spill-proof containers, gluesticks
- paper of various sizes, weights and colors
- pencils, markers, crayons, pens, erasers, small rulers, tape
- story books, crossword puzzles, dot to dot puzzles, riddles
- small dolls, matchbox cars, small animal figures
- a set of dominoes, checkers and chess, a deck of cards, cribbage board
- puzzles, Lego blocks
- small cassette player with various tapes
- a set of finger puppets
- a small sponge ball
- string and small pieces of rope

## CHAPTER ELEVEN

# TEEN AND YOUNG ADULT PLAY

Teenagers and young adults can benefit greatly from a structured recreational program that integrates socialization with self-expression. Their stage of development is often focused on what society labels mature behavior.Yet the small child that dwells within them longs to be able to play. Once structure and opportunity are provided, this age group has a wonderful time playing old childhood games and learning and inventing new ones. Many of the games already presented in this section can be used or adapted to suit this age group. This age group can usually handle competition and therefore sport activites often provide useful opportunities for the group to get in touch with their playful self. Competition can be tempered and humor can be added slowly to the activities so the group can focus on enjoyment rather than winning. Large groups can be utilized to allow the members a variety of social experiences by periodically breaking into small groups or dyads. "Who am I? How do I fit into the larger group? are questions that this developmental group is most concerned with. World affairs and local issues are also areas of interest that this age group enjoys discussing and these issues can be adapted into many of the games and exercises in this book.

Teens and young adults enjoy action in their play and they have considerably more stamina than their younger counterparts. Games and activities can be done faster or the group can work against the clock to provide more challenge. Usually this age group has a variety of talents and abilities. Leadership can be shared among them and opportunities can be provided so that these skills can be demonstrated and taught to the whole group.

## Group Activities

### ♦ MACHINES

One person begins by standing in the circle, making a motion and repeating it at regular intervals, e.g., moving arms up and down or from side to side repeatedly. The next person joins the first person and becomes attached to this person and begins his/her own motion, e.g., placing one hand on the first person's shoulder and moving the other arm in a circular motion.

The rest of the group, in turn, joins the moving persons in order to form a machine. Now the group leader suggests that each part make a sound and beginning with the person who began the game, the parts begin to make their own special sounds. Finally, the group leader asks the machine to dismantle; however, they must do this by the first player exiting first. As they leave the machine, the next in line must adapt to this loss and so on until the machine and its sound fades to the last player. This player may stay to begin a new machine.

### ♦ PEGPEN

This is a game played in many countries in many different forms. It is good fun for groups of all ages. You will need some wooden croquet balls, baseballs, or any other suitable substitutes, and a plastic bowling pin, a milk bottle or a stick in the ground.

The group can stand in a circle equal distance from the pin or at a line marked out at a suitable distance from the pin.

The object of the game is to roll your ball as close to the pin as possible. Players may knock each other's ball away from the pin.

The game can be elaborated on by adding more balls, drawing a circle around the pin and giving points to balls remaining in the circle at the end of each turn.

This game can be played with marbles or beach balls and the group can have fun creating new variations.

## ♦ BODY OBSTACLES

Instruct the group to form an obstacle course using their bodies as the obstacles. Encourage the creative use of bodies. The group leader is to make sure of safety, especially for anyone with back problems. Each person gets to go through the obstacle course and is timed. Once the group has all had a turn, suggest that now each player goes through blindfolded.

## ♦ FRIENDLY PHRASES

This is a good activity to allow group members to share their previous and current interpersonal relationships. It allows them to discuss what they see as important in friendships. This activity can give all group members useful information about each other.

Pass out the pencils and copies of the list below to the group members and ask them to complete the sentences on their own.

1. Having a friend help me to . . .
2. My best friend always . . .
3. One thing I like about my friend is . . .
4. It is important to cooperate because . . .
5. I like being with people when . . .
6. Helping others is . . .
7. One way to make a friend is . . .
8. My best friend can be counted on to . . .
9. Other people are important because . . .
10. A person I learn things from is . . .
11. My family is . . .
12. I can help most people by . . .
13. The world would be better if . . .
14. One thing I can teach someone else is . . .
15. Groups of people are . . .

Allow the group plenty of time to finish. Suggest to those who are finished early that they can draw a picture of a friend on the back. Discuss the answers with the group as well as what each members looks for in a friend.

## ♦ KIM'S GAME

Place various objects (twenty-four is a good number) on a table or flat surface and cover them with a cloth. Players come up one by one and the cloth is removed for short time (one minute is good to start). Once the time limit is up, the player is then to go and write down or draw as many objects as s/he can remember.

## ♦ NEW GAMES FROM OLD

Each player is to think of a game that is fairly simple but that is fun for this age group and then find a partner. The partners are to think of creative ways to play their games that might make them more interesting or more challenging.

## ♦ TOUCH IT

Divide the group into groups of four. One player is chosen as the chaser and the other three players join hands in order to form a triangle. Now one of the three members of the triangle is chosen as "It." The object of the game is for the chaser to touch "It" and for the triangle to prevent this from happening. The chaser may not reach through the triangle nor may s/he tag "Its" arms or hands. The chaser must touch "It" by running behind the triangle and tagging "It."

## ♦ HUMAN MASS

Divide the group up into two teams of equal numbers of members. Designate one team A and the other team B. Team A sits in a tight circle locking arms and legs until they are one human mass. Ask team A to close their eyes and imagine that they are one and cannot be taken apart. Team B is now instructed to do just that; they begin by each getting behind one member and trying to remove them from the human mass.

Rings, belts and jewelry and any potentially dangerous clothing should be removed and players are instructed not to jerk or twist arms or legs.

## ♦ BLOW YOUR SOCKS OFF

All players must be wearing socks. This is a giant free-for-all where members try to take each other's socks off. The group is divided into pairs and they begin by trying to get each other's socks off. If a person has both socks off, that person is allowed to help others.

## ♦ BODY CONTACT

Divide the group up into pairs and with each exercise have them change partners.

A. Ask the pair to stand face to face and to place their palms on their partner's palms. When both are ready they must push as hard as they can on their partner's palms.

B. Ask the pair to stand side by side with one facing in one direction and the other player facing the other way. If their right sides are touching, then they grasp right hands. If left sides are touching, they grasp left hands. When both are ready, on the count of three, each player tries to knock the other off balance. Feet must remain stationary.

C. Ask partners to lie down on their backs, side by side, with players facing opposite directions. Instruct them to get close so that their right or their left sides are touching and that they are lying hip to hip. Instruct them to grasp hands by their sides and raise their inside legs up to a full vertical position. On the count of three, after three leg raises, the players hook legs and try to flip their partner over.

D. Ask the pair to face each other and to bend forward at the waist with arms swinging free. The object of the game is to tag the other person's knee and to prevent yours from being touched. Players are allowed to move in order to dodge each other.

E. Ask the pair to squat down in front of each other with arms folded. The object of the game is to use your body to knock your partner off balance. Players are free to move and dodge one another.

## ♦ CROSSING THE SWAMP

To play this game you will need two logs approximately 3 meters long (planks 20 cm. wide are easier to walk on) as well as seven blocks of wood suitable for the planks or logs to rest on.

Divide the group into teams of eight to ten members. The imaginary swamp is 9 meters wide. The team is told to cross the swamp making use of the materials provided. They are not allowed to step off of the logs or the blocks, and they must travel the full 9 meters as a group. The first team to cross the swamp without going into the water wins.

## ♦ FLASHLIGHT TAG

You will need a flashlight to play this game; it takes on the same form as a game of tag except that it is played in the dark. The person who is designated as "It" is equipped with a flashlight. A home base is established. The person who is "It" hides his/her eyes and counts to 100 by 10's. The rest of the group hides while "It" is counting. When "It" flashes the light on one or more of the players and identifies them by name, they are caught. Those who get to home base before being caught are home free.

This game can be played by two teams. One team has flashlights, and the other team hides. Home base has a fluorescent flag which, when captured by a team member before being caught, ends the game; the teams then switch.

## ♦ SCAVENGER HUNT

Divide the group into teams. Each team gets a list of items to be collected on a hike. The first team to return home with the required number of items is the winner.

The teams can be asked to return at a specific time, those closest to the time are winners.

Each team can be given a letter of the alphabet and asked to list as many items that start with the letter that they observe on the hike.

## ♦ COMPASS HIKE

You will need a set of directions and a compass for each player/team.

A hike is made up by a neutral member of the group using the compass points as directions. For example, walk due north twenty paces, then travel east forty-five paces, and turn southwest for ten paces, etc. Each team player is given the set of directions and is required to follow the directions to a home base.

Each team can be given a different set of directions; all lead to the same location. Children and youth who are experienced at orienteering can use the compass and topographical map to find their way through a hike.

## ♦ FIRE STARTERS

This one is also for outdoors and you will need string, tinder, firewood, and matches.

A string is stretched across an open area a distance of 30 cm. off the ground. Small fire pits are constructed directly under the string. On a signal to start, each member is required to build a fire that will eventually burn the string stretched over it. The first person to burn the string is declared the winner. Each member can use only two matches to light the fire.

## ♦ CONFESSIONS

Each player needs a paper and pencil for this game. The group is instructed to sit in a circle and to print their names at the top of their sheets of paper. Then they are asked to fold the paper twice in order to cover their names. When the leader gives the signal, members are to pass their paper to the person on the left. This continues until the leader says "stop." The players are instructed to each write a true confession at the top of the sheet closest to the fold. When they are finished, they are to fold the paper again so as to cover up the confessions. The leader instructs the players to continue passing the papers until they are signalled to stop. Again the group is instructed to write down a true confession and to fold the paper. The game continues until the sheets are full. The leader signals the papers to be passed around for one last turn and then instructs them to stop. Each player unfolds the paper and in turn reads the name at the top and the list of confessions.

## ♦ FAMILY HISTORY

This activity is done over a period of time. The group members will need time to gather the necessary information. This family history goes back two generations but could go back further depending on the availability of the information. Begin by instructing group members to speak with their parents and grandparents in order to get the following information: names and birth dates of all family and extended family members; marriages, separations and divorces; deaths, dates and causes of death; occupations of all members, education, religion, and language(s) spoken; moves and reasons for moving; achievements of specific members; and adventures taken.

When this information is gathered, it can be placed on a family tree. The information is shared and presented in small groups or in the large group.

### Bibliography for Chapters Seven to Eleven

Booth, D. (1986). *Games for everyone*. Markham, ON: Pembroke Publishers.

Davies, J. (1989). *Children's games*. London, ON: Judy Piatkers Publishers.

Ferretti, F. (1975). *The great American book of sidewalks, stoop, dirt, curb and alley games*. New York: Workman Publishing.

Flugelman, F. (1976). *New games book*. New York: Doubleday.

Flugelman, F. (1981). *More new games*. New York: Doubleday.

Orlick, T. (1978). *The cooperative sports and games book*. New York: Pantheon.

Orlick, T. (1982). *The second cooperative sports and games book*. New York: Pantheon.

Phanidis, J., & Duncan, A. (1975). *Growing inside out*. Victoria, BC: Pioneer Publishing.

Robinson, J. (1983). *Activities for anyone, anytime, anywhere*. Toronto: Little, Brown, and Co.

Sernaque, V. (1988). *Classic children's games*. New York: The Bantam, Doubleday Dell Publishing Group.

Wells, H., & Canfield, D. (1976). *101 ways to improve self-concept in the classroom*. Englewood Cliffs, NJ: Prentice-Hall.

# DEVELOPING EXPERTISE

CHAPTER TWELVE

# DEALING WITH EMOTIONS

My uncle had a favorite mule, whom he named Sentient Sam. This animal was clearly his own boss. Sam did whatever he wanted, whenever he wanted. Uncle Mel and Sam were much alike in this way. Sentient Sam was a beautiful and proud beast who stuck out in the herd as an animal unique in many ways. He could be very gentle and loving and he could also be ruthless and mean. It was very difficult knowing how to be with Sam and I found myself being very fearful of his ways; yet, Sam intrigued me. I dreamt of him and thought of him for most of four years of my life. Uncle Mel knew Sam well and I got to know Sam through him. All the kids were a little afraid of "ole Sam" and we didn't venture too far into his territory. Uncle Mel took us to Sam. He told stories of how Sam had saved the herd, how he kept him from freezing and how he taught him about life. He showed us how to approach Sam and how to wait him out if he looked too scary. We felt comfortable when Uncle Mel was with us because he knew Sam. He and Sam acted like old friends; they were little kids at play and fierce rivals all in one day. They were comfortable with one another; Uncle Mel and Sam grew up together and truly loved each other.

P. Ross

**The greatest single source of difficulties in interpersonal relationships is dealing with our own and other's feelings.**

**JOHN L. WALLEN**

"Feelings reflect a need, a loss, or satiation, and are a form of energy which can be used to help us act effectively to take care of ourselves" (Hendricks & Roberts, 1977, p. 136). Denial of a need, a loss, or a satiation can cause serious imbalances. The negation and intellectual rationalization of something as real and as obvious as emotions and sensations is clearly denying the nose on one's face. Children experience pressure to control their emotions, their whims, and their sensations in most of their environments. This requires a great deal of energy, and can cause serious stress when children are not provided with outlets and vehicles with which to experience and express their emotional selves. Emotions are given labels like: negative, inappropriate, bad, undesirable, and useless. Children learn to deny, to conceal, and to suppress their feelings in order to survive. Modern medical research into cancer and heart disease show conclusively that the ability to express emotion has a great deal to do with the recovery and the prevention of these two major causes of premature death. Medical science is encouraging and is teaching its patients how to have fun and how to express emotions. Children and adults need to be able to get to know their emotions, to express and to experience them and to be a friend to them, as Uncle Mel did with Sentient Sam.

Webster's dictionary defines emotion as the affective aspect of the consciousness. Emotions are the expression of the life force within, and are a reaction to the life experience. When emotions are denied or suppressed, the individual or group is denying their own existence, and a large part of their reality. Emotions, too, are neither positive nor negative; they just are. An experience in one culture that might cause extreme pain and shame for an individual, in another culture might cause intense pleasure and pride. It is the society which labels emotions as appropriate or inappropriate, as negative or positive. The affective aspect of the typical North American child's consciousness is often suppressed. An atmosphere where children feel encouraged to show their emotions, where all emotions are acceptable, and where emotions are considered as real as the nose on the face, and as an expression of aliveness, will promote optimum developmental growth.

## ♦ Exercise 12:1

- Read the list of feelings provided. Review your past week and highlight the emotional episodes.
- Write down all those emotions that you experienced from the list of feelings.
- Put a asterisk (*) beside those emotional episodes that were powerful or in some way influential to you.
- Select each episode one by one and answer these questions:
- Did I express all my emotions?
- If not, what emotions did I repress?
- How can I express these emotions right now?
- How would I have liked to express my emotions assertively and honestly at the time I experienced them?
- Talk to a friend and develop a non-judgemental, non-blaming way of handling one of your emotional episodes.

**Feeling List**

academic
active
accurate
adaptable
adequate
adventurous
affectionate
agonizing
aggressive
alert
ambitious
ambivalent
angry
annoyed
antagonistic
anxious
apathetic
apologetic
arrogant
artistic
assertive
attractive
bashful

bitter
blissful
bold
bored
bothered
broad-minded
businesslike
calm
capable
careful
cautious
charming
cheerful
clean
clever
cold
competent
competitive
concentrating
confident
confused
conscientious
conservative

considerate
cool
cooperative
courageous
creative
curious
daring
deliberate
delightful
democratic
demure
dependable
determined
dignified
discreet
disappointed
disapproving
disbelieving
disgusted
distasteful
disoriented
dominant
eager

easy
ecstatic
efficient
elated
emotional
empty
energetic
enraged
envious
enterprising
enthusiastic
exasperated
exhausted
fair
farsighted
fearful
firm
flexible
flustered
forceful
formal
frank
friendly
frightened
frustrated
furious
generous
gentle
glad
good
grateful
gratified
grieving
guilty
happy
hateful
healthy
helpful
helpless
high
homesick
honest
hopeless
horrified
hot
humorous
hurt
hysterical
idealistic
idiotic
imaginative
independent
indifferent
industrious
informal
ingenious
innocent
inspired
intelligent
intellectual
interested
inventive
jealous
joyful
keen
kind
lazy
leisurely
lethargic
likable
logical
longing
lonely
loving
low
loyal
lustful
mad
mature
meditative
melancholy
methodical
meticulous
mild
mischievous
miserable
moderate
modest
natural
negative
nervous
obliging
obstinate
optimistic
organized
outgoing
pained
paranoid
patient
peaceful
peeved
persevering
petrified
pleasant
poised
polite
practical
precise
progressive
prudish
powerful
purposeful
puzzled
rage
rational
realistic
reasonable
reflective
regretful
rejected
relaxed
reliable
remorseful

reserved
resourceful
responsible
restless
retiring
robust
sad
satisfied
self-confident
self-controlled
sensible
sensitive
serious
sexy
scared
skeptical
shocked
sheepish
sincere
smug
sociable
sorrowful
spontaneous
spunky
stable
strong
sure
suspicious
sympathetic
tactful
tenacious
terrified
thorough
thoughtful
threatened
tolerant
tough
trusting
trustworthy
unaffected
unassuming
undecided
understanding
uneasy
unexcitable
uninhibited
unsettled
verbal
versatile
vulnerable
warm
weepy
wholesome
wise
witty
worried
zany

This list can be used in many of the exercises, activities, and games in this text. It provides children and youth with an extensive list of feelings, emotions, and strengths to help them appreciate the subtleties in these areas.

There is a popular misconception that some feelings are bad and others are good. Adults convey this message to children and, eventually, some grow up believing that it is bad to get angry, to cry, to feel afraid and, in some instances, to feel pleasure. This same understanding is carried on with thoughts and behaviors to the extreme, where some children see themselves in a type of schizophrenia where there exists the good me and the bad me. When this misconception is applied to gender stereotypes, we find males expressing anger and females expressing sadness more than any other emotions. These predominant emotions are often secondary in relation to the original emotion. This happens in the male child who is prompted to express anger even when he feels afraid, sad, or alone. The female child also experiences this when she is prompted to express sadness and fear through her tears when actually she may be feeling angry, frustrated or misunderstood. Another misconception is that it is acceptable to feel anger, but not to be too angry, or to feel sorrow, but not feel too much sorrow, or to feel grief, but not to grieve too much. This misconception also interferes with the essential information and messages that emotions convey. That is, they tell us of our experiences.

Children need an environment that allows them to become familiar with all of their emotions and to learn to decode the messages they send and receive. This will allow them opportunities to develop effective, socially acceptable, behavioral strategies and thought processes in response to their experiences in life. Child and youth care professionals need to promote an environment that makes the expression of emotions a natural and spontaneous act.

The expression of emotion does need to be structured and controlled within socially acceptable parameters. The best way to structure the expression of emotion is to first experience and understand the emotion and its messages.

The basic message of most emotions is the expression of a want or need or a satisfaction of a want or need. Emotions tell us what it is that we want or need which give us clues on how we should behave, think, and live in the world. Emotions often tell us what we need to change and what we should not change. They tell us how we react to certain individuals and in certain situations. They are a form of energy that can motivate and create, that can immobilize and destroy. When emotions are accepted, expected, and cherished, the individual is acknowledged. The affective aspect of the conscious self and the unconscious self is reflected or transmitted by the emotions and, when these are revered, then so is the individual.

## ♦ Exercise 12:2

- Find a relaxed area and get as comfortable as possible. Begin with a favourite relaxation exercise.
- Once relaxed, start with the sense of sight and ask yourself the following questions.
- "What do feelings look like?" Go through the primary feelings (i.e., sadness, anger, fear, happiness) one by one and decide what they look like.
- If you want, now include the more subtle categories of emotions such as embarrassment, surprise, loss, frustration, exhaustion, exhilaration and so on. Consult the list used in exercise 12:1.

- "What do feelings sound like?" As with sight, recall the primary feelings first and then the more subtle feelings.
- "What do feelings taste like?"
- "What do feelings smell like?"
- "What do feelings feel like?" This is feeling in the tactile sense.
- You may want to write down your answers to the questions and discuss them and your experiences with a friend.

Emotions not only affect the psychological self and the sociological self, they also have effects on the physiological self. "One of the ways we stop ourselves from experiencing our feelings is through body tension and blocks" (Hendricks & Roberts, 1977, p. 136). The physical self, in order to control rage, may create musculature tension in the back of the neck, in the shoulders, or in any other part of the anatomy. This tension becomes the physiological reaction to that particular emotion. The blocks also appear in our breathing patterns. The body's way to control fear or anxiety, for example, might show up in the breathing patterns of an individual. A block in a breathing pattern manifests itself with limited or restricted breathing, shallow breathing, or gasping. Breath is life giving and, when breathing patterns are blocked or stopped, this directly affects the physiological self. The technique of controlling emotions by tensing the body or by restricting breathing only adds more stress to the individual, and is a maladaptive strategy. There is an interrelationship between emotion and motion. When motion is restricted, so too is emotion. Muscular tensions and erratic breathing patterns restrict motion. A more productive strategy for structuring emotions is with movement of the physical self expressing the emotional self. The expression of emotion through movement and the arts, through imagery, fantasy and relaxation, and by means of intellectual discussion and experimental learning are all effective ways to channel and structure emotional experiences.

## ♦ Exercise 12:3

- Find a comfortable place, take a relaxed position, and relax your body.
- Close your eyes and imagine that you are able to scan your body like a C.A.T. Scan. Start with your feet and very slowly and very thoroughly scan your feet for signs of tension or the effects of stress.

- Travel the length of your body, scanning portions at a time.
- Take particular care when you scan your organs to notice the areas of your body where you hold tension.
- When you have completed this, make a diagram of your body and mark on it the parts or areas where you noticed the tension.
- Are there concentrated areas?
- Where are your big stress areas on the chart?
- Examine your diagram and think how you could exercise/stimulate the areas of stress.
- Make a list of four ways you could relieve the tension in each area identified.
- Make a resolution to try to reduce stress and to express physically what you experience emotionally.

Children are much freer in their expression of emotion than adults and this sometimes frightens the adult group leader, especially if the feeling is a painful one. As well, this fearful reaction can, in turn, frighten the child. Intense feelings of loss, fear, rage, grief, and so on can be very uncomfortable feelings to talk about. In order for children to become more comfortable with these feelings, the child and youth care professional needs to become skilled at helping children to talk about their feelings. The first obvious step is for the adult to become comfortable with his/her feelings. Once that is accomplished, there are numerous techniques designed to allow groups of children to make friends with all of their emotions. In this way, children can learn appropriate ways to express their feelings without inhibition, and to develop a respect and a love for themselves as sensitive beings.

## ♦ Exercise 12:4

- Answer the following questions:
- How do I express anger, sorrow, fear, happiness, loss, pride, jealousy, etc?
- How can I learn to be more expressive and less reactive to feelings?
- Do I have a best friend, skilled helper, counsellor or therapist with whom I can explore my emotional experiences?
- Do I have healthy ways of expressing myself emotionally?

- Keep a journal of your emotions for one week and keep a pictorial record of a series of emotional events. List what you can do to express emotions and then go out and do it.

Group experiences that focus on emotions and thoughts in a logical and sequential way can be awkward for both child and adult at first. The intellectualizing of emotions can also be traumatizing in some way. The child's act of sharing his internal world, fact, or fancy should be treated with reverence and respect. The group climate and milieu are essential areas of consideration for the success of feeling groups. The group must have achieved a basic level of trust in the adult leader, and varying levels of trust with each other in order to be able to freely express emotions with group members. The milieu needs to reflect an atmosphere of calm and warmth. The meeting place should be warm and friendly. The size of the group should be small, and the intellectual level of the group participants should be homogeneous.

When discussing feelings, it is useful to have group members seated in a circle. This allows for better eye contact with one another, and members are positioned on the same physical plane. If the group is seated on the floor, cushions or mats can be provided for their comfort. The concept of the circle provides a feeling of unity and equality. Even if the group is on the twelfth floor of a high rise, sitting on the floor will bring the child closer to the earth. This closeness to the earth has calming, comforting, and non-threatening qualities that are useful in this type of group activity.

If the group is just starting to discuss feelings in a structured way, many will need guidance on how to behave. Here are some useful guidelines and points of discussion to present the group:

- Feelings are real, and it's okay to have them.
- There are no right/wrong, bad/good feelings.
- Group members have the right to choose not to talk about their feelings.
- Feelings discussed in the group are private for the group members only and are not talked about outside of the group.
- When one group member is speaking, the other members need to be silent and to listen.
- Group members should agree to refrain from judging each other's feelings, thoughts, and behaviors.

Discussions concerning emotions do not always have to take on the structure presented here. In fact, impromptu discussions can often be less threatening and more productive. Finally, when structured activities are presented to the group, it is best to monitor their effects on group members. Some children, particularly those who have been traumatized, can be reminded of their experiences in these discussions. The group leader may need to provide some added support for that child. It may mean spending some time alone with the child; or it may mean alerting the child's caregiver. Feelings are very personal and wonderful experiences. Their expression and symbolization in group process can be meaningful and can help the child to mature.

As in all good activity programming, pacing of the group and the activities allows the group to begin at its level of understanding and maturity and to progress at its own pace. When planning for these types of more sedentary exercises, the programmer may want to reverse the order suggested in Chapter Three: Program Design. The warm-up to the activity could be a centering or relaxation activity, and the cool-down might include an active game.

Emotions can be represented through all modalities. A picture, a color, a movement, a shape, can all be stimuli for emotions. A song, a sound, a voice, a smell, a taste, a way of being touched can cause feelings. Therefore, when discussing emotions in a group, all modalities represented in the presentation of the topic, and in the discussion, make for a richer and fuller experience of the feelings.

Use happy pictures, songs, sounds, smells, tastes, etc. when discussing happiness. Pictures of people weeping, dark colors, sad songs, slow and serious voice tones, all enhance a discussion on sorrow. Discussions on sorrow as well as fear end nicely with a group hug for comfort and support. Yelling out loud, drawing angry pictures, and stamping your feet make discussions on anger more real. Scary music, dark and bright colors, pictures of hospitals, accidents, or fires make the atmosphere more amenable to expressing fears. When using these techniques, certain cautions must be adhered to. Emotional levels of the group must be respected at all times. Techniques, such as pictures, sounds, and sensations, should be introduced one at a time. It is important not to overload any one emotion for the child. Slow and easy steps when introducing the different modalities is very important to the emotional well-being of the child.

Recognition, validation, support, comfort, acceptance, amelioration, and more can be gained through healthy and open discussions about the humanness of being a child.

**A person who lives a life immune to hurt lives a life immune to joy.**

**DAVID VISCOTT**

## Activities

### ♦ EMOTIONS

This exercise is a good opener for new groups or groups that have been apart for some time. Group members can be alerted ahead of time to bring favorite objects or fearful objects, etc., to the group discussion.

Instruct the group to form a circle and to review the rules of conduct in the group in order to reaffirm their importance to group safety. The beginning point for this group depends on the level of trust and familiarity among the members, and on their intellectual level of functioning. Here are some suggestions:

(a) Using photographs or sketches that present people experiencing emotion, ask the group to comment on the perceived emotion;

(b) What makes people angry, embarrassed, etc.?

(c) What makes you sad, frightened, etc.?

(d) Concentrate on a time when you felt lonely, misunderstood, confused, etc. Where did you feel it in your body? What part of your body is affected when you feel angry, frightened, etc.? What did you think when you felt sad, lonely, etc.? What did you do? How would you like to have behaved?

The following is a format for a basic discussion on anger with a group of eight- to ten-year-old children:

Today we are going to talk about anger. We all have times when we get really angry at someone or about something. It is okay to be angry, and to let people know that we are angry, as long as we do not use our anger to hurt anyone or ourselves. Let's all take a few minutes to remember a time when we were angry, really angry. Go back and remember that time and ask yourself:

1. Who were you angry at?
2. How did you let them know you were angry?
3. Where did you feel your angry feelings?
4. What do you look like when you are angry?
5. What angry sounds do you make?

Each child and adult takes a turn and discusses his anger in terms of the five headings listed above.

We all have times when we are angry and we all have different ways of showing our anger. It is okay to be angry and to express our anger appropriately. It is not okay to hurt someone or ourselves when we are angry.

(e) Draw how it feels to be embarrassed, neglected, frightened, etc. Children can experiment with abstract drawings, collages, etc.

## ♦ DO THIS, DO THAT

This is a good role play that will allow children to experience different emotions and to discuss them within the group.

Ask the group to pair up. Have each pair, one at a time, act out ways to ask someone for something. One child will do the asking, and the other will respond. Give each a turn at both asking and responding.

(1) Pick up toys.
(2) Clean room.
(3) Feed dog.
(4) Hang up jacket.
(5) Take out garbage.
(6) Help sister dress her doll.

(You may add some of your own as well.)

Discuss how each person felt in each situation. Discuss the difference (at a feeling level) between requests, commands, and straight statements.

## ♦ PASS THE OBJECT

This allows children to project their feelings, or imagined feelings, onto an inanimate object.

Collect a series of objects that you feel would be most provocative to the group members, e.g., an apple, a stuffed toy, an empty glass, car keys, beer bottle, cigarette, etc. Instruct the group to sit down and form a circle. Pass one of the objects to a member of the group, and ask them to comment on how the object might feel or think. Each group member gets a turn to express a feeling or thought. Select another object and repeat the procedure.

## ♦ I GET WHAT I WANT

This activity allows children to explore some of the means, at different levels of awareness, that they use in order to get their wants and needs met.

Ask the group to form dyads and select A and B. Instruct A to imagine an object that is special to that person. Next, A is to discuss with B what this object is, and why it is so important. Now B is to try in all the ways s/he can think of, to persuade A to give him/her this object. Give them a time limit of two minutes. When the time is up, ask each pair to switch roles and to repeat the exercise.

When the group has completed the entire exercise, discuss the following in dyads:

(1) What feelings did this exercise bring up for A and B?
(2) What techniques or tactics did each use to try to persuade the other?
(3) What techniques or tactics did you not try?
(4) What are the most useful ways that you believe will assist you in getting your wants and needs met?

The discussion can be brought to the entire group in terms of question (4).

## ♦ IT'S ALL IN THE WAY YOU SAY IT

This exercise allows children to experience how their requests and demands affect others and how requests and demands of others affect them.

Instruct the group to form dyads and select who will be A and who will be B. A is to communicate to B the following requests or statements:

(1) Give help in a task.
(2) Not to play in a certain area.
(3) That B is not playing fairly.
(4) That the group does not want B to play with them today.
(5) To share a particular treat.

When this is completed, ask the dyads to switch roles and to repeat the exercise. Once the whole group has experienced the role of both A and B, they can discuss how they felt with their partner when s/he made demands and requests. Discuss feelings in the larger group. If there was a particular way of being asked to do something that upset you or made you feel like you did not want to comply, discuss this with your partner. How would you have liked to be asked? Try this different way and discuss it with your partner. Discuss, involving the whole group, effective ways of asking for what you want and need.

## ♦ BE YOUR FAVORITE PERSON

This guided fantasy allows the children to get in touch with those qualities, feelings, and ways of behaving that they hold as admirable. It also gives insight into how each child wishes to be seen by others.

Relax the group using a favorite relaxation exercise or one that is available in Chapter 13.

- Feeling warm and peaceful, let your mind drift off to a land where you feel safe.
- In a minute, I am going to ask you to think about your most favorite person, the kind of person you would most like to be like. Think about that now.
- This person can be someone from the neighborhood, or someone from T.V., or a singer, whoever you wish it to be.
- Study this person very closely. How do they act?
- How do they feel?
- What do they say?
- How do they look?
- Now step into that picture and become that person. Be aware of how it feels to be that person.
- In a few minutes I am going to ask you all to sit up and be the person you most like. I am going to ask you all, one by one, to introduce yourself once everyone is sitting in a circle.

Once the group is sitting, go around and have everyone, one at a time, stand up in the center of the circle and introduce themselves, saying a few words about what they do, etc. When that is finished, have the whole group get up and talk casually with one another. Give them two to three minutes to interact. Ask the group to lie back down again and to become as relaxed as they were before. Instruct them,

- I want you to recall how it felt to be your favorite person.
- Now I want you to step back out of the picture and to become yourself again.
- You will be surprised to find, in the days to come, that many of the good things about that person will show up in you. Say one last good-bye to that favorite person.
- Now I want you to come back to the room slowly, open your eyes, and sit up when you feel ready.

Ask the group the following questions:

What was your experience like?

What qualities do you admire in this person?

How could you develop those qualities in yourself?

How do you feel physically when you imagine yourself to be this person?

## ♦ SELF-PORTRAIT

This is an art exercise that provides an avenue for children to share their feelings of self-worth with the group.

Instruct the group members to create a self-portrait. It can be a silhouette, a figure drawing, a collage, or an abstract. When the group members have completed their self-portraits, each person is to display their picture and to introduce themselves by describing their likes and dislikes, strengths and weaknesses, tastes in music and clothes, etc. The group members are free to ask questions appropriate to the self-portrait.

## ♦ THE CONTINUUM OF FEELINGS

This exercise gives children a chance to evaluate their feelings at the moment or how they might feel in specific situations. When this exercise is repeated over a period of time, children become more aware of the continuum that their feelings run along. As well, in more advanced discussions, they can become more aware of how intensely they feel, and more aware of those feelings that they avoid.

Ask the group to rate themselves individually in the following areas. This rating can refer to their overall assessment of themselves as to how they feel at the moment. The rating is from one to ten, e.g., happy/sad, one would be most happy and ten would be most sad:

(1) happy/sad
(2) angry/calm
(3) fearful/fearless
(4) aggressive/passive
(5) talkative/quiet
(6) friendly/unfriendly
(7) worrisome/carefree
(8) confident/unsure

## ♦ IMAGINARY DOCTOR

This activity is an excellent way of centering the child, and giving him/her a vehicle for contacting his/her inner wisdom.

Relax the group with a favorite relaxation exercise.

- ♦ Now that you are feeling quiet and relaxed, I want you to go off in your mind, to a spot where you feel safe and comfortable. Go there now.
- ♦ Notice any sounds or voices.
- ♦ Take in all the colors of this place. Be aware of how you are feeling and how it feels to be here.
- ♦ Get a clear picture and make it any way you want.

- In a short time, you are going to meet a very special person in your place. This person will be very wise and will be especially for you. We will call this person your imaginary doctor. Take all the time you need to experience this person. If the imaginary doctor does not materialize in your mind, just make believe.
- Once you have become aware of this person, ask if there is anything special or important that you must do.
- Ask any questions you want.
- Spend as much time as you need to finish with your imaginary doctor.
- Take one last look, speak one last word, get one last feeling for what it is like.
- In a minute I am going to ask you to come back. Do what you need to do.
- Come back slowly, remembering your experience.

Ask the group members the following questions:

What was the experience like for you?

Describe your imaginary doctor.

Did you get any advice from your imaginary doctor?

In closing, remind the group that they can contact this person when they need help.

All they have to do is to lie down, relax, and start to recall this experience and their imaginary doctor.

## ♦ ANIMAL FANTASY

This is a good exercise for exploring self-esteem. There are several ways to approach this exercise. Here is one example.

Ask the group to form a circle and conduct a relaxation exercise with them. Say to them,

Now that you have been able to relax your body, I want you to slow down your thoughts and imagine an animal, any kind of animal you want

- Slowly begin to imagine your animal.
- What is it doing when you first see it?
- What does it look like?
- Is your animal making any sounds?
- Is it saying anything to itself? Are there any sounds or noises?
- Now I want you to become that animal.
- Just imagine yourself stepping into the picture and becoming that animal.
- How are you feeling as the animal?
- Move around and explore your worlds.

- Can you smell anything?
- Taste anything?
- Enjoy being that animal.
- Is your home nearby? What is it like?
- In a few seconds, I am going to ask you to come back, so explore for one last minute.
- Now I want you to come slowly back and be yourself again.
  Slowly . . . When you are back, you can open your eyes . . . Now sit up when you are ready.
  Ask the group the following questions:
  What did your animal look like?
  Could you hear any sounds?
  Was the animal saying anything to themselves?
  What did it feel like to be that animal?
  Could you smell or taste anything?
  What was your house like?

## Bibliography for DEALING WITH EMOTIONS

Dreikurs, R. (1964). *Children: The challenge*. New York: Hawthorn Books.

Egan, G. (1986). *The skilled helper*. Belmont, CA: Wadsworth Inc.

Ginott, H. (1972). *Teacher and child*. New York: MacMillan.

Hendricks, G., & Roberts, T. (1977). *The second centering book*. Englewood Cliffs, NJ: Prentice-Hall.

Viscott, D. (1976). *The language of feelings*. New York: Pocket Books.

Wallen, J., & Rogers, C. (1946). *Counselling with returned servicemen*. New York: McGraw Hill.

Yardley, A. (1988). *Senses and sensitivity*. London: Rubicon Publishing.

CHAPTER THIRTEEN

# RELAXATION, IMAGERY, AND GUIDED FANTASY

My grandfather was a very patient man and he prided himself on being a good problem solver. "When matters get confusing, son, and you're not sure which way to go, remember these words: "SLOW DOWN, FEEL, and THINK!" Grandpa was known for his dramatics and he usually got quite animated during this treatise.

Slow down, slow down your movements and your breathing. Relax those good muscles of yours and sit or lie yourself down. Get comfortable and when everything is quiet on your outside, start to slow down your insides. Decrease your heart rate and allow your thoughts to drift, your organs to rest and the very tissue of the cells in your body to soften. Feel your breath enter and escape from your lungs as your whole being begins to experience total relaxation.

Now it's time to experience your emotions. Allow your feelings to enter your awareness. Do not block them, just allow them to surface on their own. Laugh, cry, shriek, pound, tremble; whatever it takes to give them expression. Imagine your emotions flowing out of your being until there is only quiet peace.

All is ready now for creative thinking. Focus your awareness on what appears to be the problem. Open your mind to any and all solutions, allowing your thoughts to flow freely. Write these solutions down and decide on the three you feel will be most useful. The problem is halfway solved now.

Act on your new awareness and remember: slow down . . .think . . . feel.

**Relaxing images actually produce physiological changes in the body. A person can deliberately call to mind an image . . . to produce mental and physical relaxation.**
**MIKE & NANCY SAMUELS**

Relaxation, that state of rest or slowing down of the physiological self combined with imagery which is the ability to construct visual, auditory, and kinesthetic representations of reality in the brain, form the conditions necessary for guided fantasy. Guided fantasy was Grandfather's favourite technique. He would relax me with his manner and language in order to lead me on an internal voyage of discovery.

This chapter introduces the reader to the concepts and practical uses of relaxation, imagery, and guided fantasy in the practice of child and youth care. It provides the child and youth care professional with experiences that will assist in a better appreciation of the relaxation, imagery, and guided fantasy processes. Techniques in each of these areas are provided to aid the seasoned play facilitator to offer these types of experiences to children and youth.

The use of relaxation, imagery, and guided fantasy as a method of improving and enriching lives, is as old as human kind. Socrates emphasized to his young students that their first duty was to relax and to reassure their patients. Women from the Lakota Indian tribe of North America whispered cheerful thoughts to their young children as they slept; these were words to comfort, to relax, and to strengthen the child. Buddist monks use relaxation and imagery to become more spiritually aware. The medical sciences utilize the power of relaxation, imagery, and guided fantasy to promote and sustain health.

Children and youth can be taught to relax themselves as a way of enhancing their state of well-being. They can be trained to use imagery to augment their performances in academics, athletic, and artistic endeavours. They can benefit from the stress-releasing and problem-solving qualities of guided fantasy. Children and youth can benefit in many areas of their lives by experiencing and using these techniques.

## ♦ Exercise 13:1

♦ Lie down on the floor or other flat surface. If possible, lie on your back with your legs slightly apart, your arms by your sides and your spine completely straight. You may also sit down in a comfortable position that will allow your body maximum support.

- Close your eyes and begin to relax each group of muscles from your toes to your head.
- Travel from toes to head and back again slowly. All the while sending soothing messages to each muscle, tendon, nerve, and organ to let go and relax.
- Once you find yourself relaxed and your mind is drifting, begin to focus your attention on some of the people who have influenced your life in a positive way.
- Send a mental "thank you" to each person to express your appreciation.
- Slowly reawaken your physical self, giving your body and mind all the time it needs to integrate the experience.

## RELAXATION

In the late 1960s Dr. Herbert Benson of Harvard Medical School categorized a series of physiological changes and called them the relaxation response. He noticed that when relaxed, his subjects decreased their oxygen consumption, decreased their carbon dioxide production, lowered their blood pressure, decreased their heart rates, lowered the levels of lactate in their blood systems, and intensified their alpha brain waves (Beary & Benson, 1974). "One of the implications of Benson's work is the understanding that a person is able to control in a general way, their body physiology" (Samuel & Samuel, 1975, p. 222). This ability provides opportunities for children and youth to lower their levels of stress and lessen the effects that stress is having on their bodies. Dr. David Elkind, in his book, *The Hurried Child*, points out the dramatic increase in stress levels for the children and youth in our countries (Elkind, 1988).

The pressure to grow up, to achieve academically, to be future oriented, asks children to become adult-like before their emotional and intellectual selves have had time to develop. Parents, teachers, media, communications, and society in general, are expecting more and more of children than they are developmentally capable, resulting in excessive stress to achieve the impossible.

Children in dysfunctional families are under such extensive stress and duress that they become hypervigilant. They are so tuned to the emotional climate of the family that they are sensitive to the slightest discomfort in their parents and siblings.

Quiet and calming activities presented in peaceful and trusting environments provide children and youth opportunities to slow down and to forget about the future and to experience the present. Relaxation can be mastered by most children and youth; however, obvious differences in developmental levels dictate the length and type of relaxation methods used. The ability to relax oneself easily, quickly, and to a deep level of relaxation can have a considerable effect on the level of stress maintained.

Relaxation decreases stress by releasing muscle and skeletal tension, lowering the intensity of stress to the sympathetic nervous system, slowing down the demand to the cardiovascular system, optimizing the respiratory system, and increasing the effectiveness of the immune system.

In the physical sense, the ability to lower stress on the central nervous system is crucial to many forms of heart and respiratory problems. It can drastically lower the possibility of strokes and various forms of stress-related diseases.

On a cognitive level, relaxation can assist the child in many areas of their academic life by increasing memory, by intensifying creative thinking, and by promoting assimilation of learning. Children will find less difficulty in thinking and problem solving in the areas of mathematics and physics if they are able to slow down and concentrate.

## ♦ Exercise 13:2

- Find yourself a comfortable spot and take all the time you need to squirm around until you feel settled and relaxed.
- When it feels right, soften your gaze and focus your vision on one spot, one object before you.
- As you softly gaze at the object, quiet your thoughts and in your own time quietly close your eyes.
- With your eyes closed, begin to focus your attention on breathing.
- As you inhale, be aware of the air entering your lungs, filling your blood system with oxygen.
- And as you exhale, concentrate on the air that expels from your lungs, releasing the carbon dioxide to nurture the plant life.
- Try to fill the lung cavities so that there is air in the top and bottom portions
- and exhale so that the lung is completely empty.
- Control your breathing so that you are able to fill the bottom portions of the lungs first, then the middle, and finally, the upper portions.

- As you exhale, empty the lungs from the top portions to the bottom portions of the lungs.
- Continue this technique for ten breaths.
- De-focus your concentration on your breathing and allow your breath to regulate itself.
- Now, as you inhale, imagine that your breath is travelling through your body
- in through your nostrils to the crown of your head and down through your throat to the tips of your toes
- and as you exhale, feel the air escape from every pore of your being.
- Use this technique for ten breaths.
- When you are ready, slowly awaken yourself, taking all the time you need to reintegrate yourself to your surroundings before you open your eyes and become slowly accustomed to your external reality.

## Practical Uses of Relaxation

Relaxation techniques with children greatly increase the child's ability to sleep soundly. Soothing words, physical touch, relaxing stories, and language allow the overstimulated child opportunities to prepare themselves for restful sleep.

Meal times can be more relaxing, thus increasing digestion and health to the body. One might prepare children and youth for meal time by listening to the day's events before the meal is served, by playing quiet relaxing music before and during the meal, by slowing down their activity levels, through hugging and giving back rubs before the meals. Finally, a prayer to give thanks to the provider of life and recognition to the cooks and attendants, sets up more possibilities for healthier meals.

In addition to the earlier comments made about stress, children and youth can be assisted by relaxation before writing tests or examinations, before public speaking or talking with parents, when coping with the stress of doctor and dentist appointments, while coping in dysfunctional families, when dealing with the effects of trauma, poverty, separation and divorce, or while dealing with situations of adjustment and change to their environment. Relaxation can be used to enhance creativity by slowing the child or youth down before the creative experience.

There are a number of relaxation techniques and exercises in this book and in the activity section at the end of this chapter that can be incorporated into daily routines, school curriculums, and leisure activities that can make life more meaningful, less stressful, and more pleasurable.

## ♦ Exercise 13:3

- Make a list of your daily activities and routines from the time you wake up until the time you sleep at night.
- Place a check mark or star beside the routines or activities that you find relaxing.
- Approximate the length of time for each relaxing activity and routine.
- Calculate how much you relax in your waking hours.
- Ask yourself this question. "Do I wake up in the mornings feeling rested?"
- Go back to your list and place an arrow or an X beside daily activities that need to become less stressful.
- Brainstorm and strategize how you could incorporate simple relaxation exercises or techniques to release the stress.
- Incorporate your new ideas into your daily life and periodically evaluate by repeating this exercise.

## IMAGERY

Imagery is an internal process that requires the individual to see with the mind's eye, hear within, and to feel internally. It involves hallucinations of the senses by conjuring images, sounds, feelings, and sensations. The child creates an internal reality or representation of that reality by using internal processes. Imagery can be as simple as remembering and picturing in the mind a familiar face, or hearing a familiar voice, or feeling a familiar feeling and it can be as complex as seeing, hearing, and feeling an entire episode or series of episodes in the child's life. Children can be taught to image themselves being successful, confident, and clear thinking. Imagery requires a state of internal relaxation and concentration. Although imagery can be used when the body is active, to begin, children should learn to relax their bodies as well as their minds when they are sitting, lying, or standing passively. Imagery is a part of all guided fantasy exercises and can be used individually to help the child focus on one particular task. This focusing of the attention can help the child to learn more about the task or situation.

Imagery is usually preceded by a form of relaxation exercise to help the child to make images. There are some exercises and techniques throughout this book that require imagery and there are more specific exercises for children and youth in the activity section found at the end of this chapter.

Imagery, like relaxation, can be used in conjunction with other activities in order to make them more meaningful, effective, or less stressful.

## ♦ Exercise 13:4

- Recall a difficult situation from the past that is likely to occur again for you in the future, e.g., confronting a co-worker, a job interview, dealing with a difficult adolescent.
- Find a comfortable spot and relax yourself fully.
- Recall the incident from the past and become aware of all that was visible at that time.
- Now remember what was said, any background noise or anything you were saying to yourself.
- Now recapture your emotional and tactile awareness at the time.
- Once you have a real and rich representation of that time, imagine yourself as an independent observer and recall the situation from start to finish.
- Write down or articulate to a friend what you observed that was interesting or new.
- Relax yourself again and imagine that you have all the internal abilities to be successful in a similar situation in the future.
- Create such a situation using imagery and see yourself being successful.
- Arrange the situation so that your objectives are met fully to your satisfaction.
- Repeat this process several times until you have a successful vision of the future.

## GUIDED FANTASY

Guided Fantasy is a structured form of imagery where children are told a story or given a series of directions that allows them to fantasize or to recreate what is being said into their internal experience.

In a guided fantasy the child is asked to experience and benefit from the story in a way that best suits that individual. This type of approach leaves the child open to all possible variables of benefiting from the experience. Guided fantasy is usually preceded by a relaxation exercise. An example of an introduction to a guided fantasy would be:

Now that you are here and relaxed in a positive way, I want to tell you a story. You can become characters in the story, if you wish; or, you can pretend to be objects in the story; or, you can listen and learn; or, you can drift off to your own story world, enjoying and learning all the time what is important for you as a happy, healthy and lovable child. You may choose to make pictures and sounds, and smells and tastes and feelings out of the words you hear to make the story real. You may choose not to choose. Breathe deeply and feel comfortable while listening to my voice.

In the example, the dialogue gives the child a series of suggestions as choices in terms of ways of responding. All of these choices are presented as ways in which the child can benefit from the story. The element of choice is very important in guided fantasy because it allows the child to easily respond to what is being asked. The statement "You may choose not to choose" covers the child who is experiencing difficulty relating to any of the choices given. The introduction to the guided fantasy should further relax the child and prepare him/her to gain the most from the experience. The idea of benefiting from the story or fantasy is suggested so that any morals, examples, ideals, or directions presented in the story might be attended to by the child.

Guided fantasies can also be stories that the child and youth care professional has written especially for a specific child or group of children. The adult must always be aware of the power of guided fantasy and take precautions when dealing with material that might re-awaken traumatic or otherwise negative experiences from the child's past. One way to guard against the possibility of children reacting to an otherwise harmless story line or subject matter in a negative way, is to prepare them for possible adverse reactions to the fantasy and to provide the option that they may open their eyes and sit quietly if necessary. This element of choice should be made clear in the introduction to the guided fantasy. The subject of using story and metaphor as a teaching or healing technique is discussed further in Chapter Fourteen on storytelling.

Centering, a form of guided fantasy, is a technique which helps the child to feel balanced, confident, and in charge. It focuses the child's energy on a given task or subject so that they may deal with it in the best way that they know how. A centering exercise is preceded by a relaxation exercise and by an introduction. The introduction to a centering exercise is similar to that used in a guided fantasy in that a series of choices are presented to the child. The choices relate to the state of being called, being centered or being balanced.

The state of being centered is one of strength, calmness, concentration, and relaxation. "There is a feeling of balance, a feeling of inner strength that we feel when we are *centered*" (Hendricks & Wills, 1975, p. xi). In *The Centering Book* (1975) and *The Second Centering Book* (1977), Gay Hendricks presents centering as a way for children and adults to achieve "a solid integration of mind and body" (Hendricks & Wills, 1975, p. xi). These publications are excellent sources of centering exercises. This state of being is more than feeling calm and relaxed, it is more of a concentration of energy and a combining of inner resources. This type of focus of energy can be used to help the child achieve a desired goal.

A child can experience various states of this centered feeling. A physical center, where the child feels grounded to his/her environment is sometimes referred to as grounding. Many grounding techniques use imagery and visualization in order to assist the child to reach this state of physiological harmony. The child in this state is asked to experience a somewhat heightened state of physical awareness while imagining an absorption of strength and energy from the environment. This technique assists the child in strengthening his/her sense of physical awareness. Through its repeated use, a child can begin to feel more comfortable and confident with his/her physical self-proficiency. This skill has vast implications for the physiological health of the child.

Cognitive or intellectual centering focuses a relaxed mind and body on specific subject material or concepts. It can be a form of brain storming to ask the child to free-flow think in respect to a specific theme. It can be used as a way of desensitizing feelings or emotional blocks which hamper learning. It has obvious benefit to the classroom which makes it popular with educators. Its potential outside the classroom is far reaching when it is applied to socialization, the arts, mental health, self-concept, and countless other areas.

Emotional centering allows children to experience a balance in their emotional life. Its techniques of integrating mind and body allow children to make better choices in their emotional responses. When used extensively it presents the child with wide ranges of emotional experiences and the ability to deal effectively with emotion. Some children become so skilled in this technique that they can center themselves at will.

Centering can also take on a spiritual or meditative aspect. The child can be asked to center him/herself on God, the Universe, Nature, Beauty, the Meaning of Life, Death, Light, and so on. The nature of this type of activity allows children to experience their own individual awareness around certain ideals, and in time, they are able to express these awarenesses in order to apply them to their own thoughts and behaviors.

## Conducting Exercises in Relaxation, Imagery, and Guided Fantasy

When beginning a relaxation, imagery, or guided fantasy exercise, try to use your voice to match the child's state of awareness. If they are loud and excited, begin with a loud and excited voice. If they are quiet and slow moving, adjust your voice and timing to suit them. Once you have matched their state sufficiently, you can lead them to the state that you feel is most beneficial for the particular exercise.

Like any new skill, children will need to become accustomed to the technique and should be asked to participate in short exercises of relaxation, imagery, or guided fantasy and you can slowly work them up to the time frame necessary for them to benefit most from the exercise. A slow rhythmic pace is important to allow the children to respond. Some children have a lot of difficulty relaxing at first and may need additional help. Holding a teddy bear or stuffed animal can help. A gentle hand on the shoulder and in some cases, a back rub, helps the child to slow down. The use of familiar storylines or themes can help children to relax as well as repetition of the same exercise.

When using relaxation, imagery, and guided fantasy, try to make your instructions fit the child's immediate experience. If the children are lying down, have the character or characters lying down. If they are fidgeting or moving their feet, have the character do the same. If it is warm or the sun is shining down on them, have this fit into the storyline as well. This technique is more useful at the beginning to assist those children who are having difficulty with relaxing or participating. Another useful technique is to include statements that further replicate the child's reality, e.g., "The sun was shining and she crossed and uncrossed her legs" or "Lying on the ground, he felt the sun shine on his face." You can also make statements that verify the child's external and internal realities, e.g., "As she crossed and uncrossed her legs, she wondered what would come next"; "The sun is shining and her brain was active"; or "Lying down, she began to slowly, very slowly, think peaceful thoughts." This technique allows children to make easy small steps towards relaxing, imagining, and fantasizing in a way that fits in with their present state of awareness. Eventually, the child care professional includes less of the external experience and more of the internal experience until the group or individual is fully relaxed or in sync with the fantasy.

Voice tone can be varied to suit the child's present state and then slowly altered to a slow rhythmic pace with increasingly longer pauses. The breaking up of sentences also allows the child to slow down or to catch up. A good technique is to match the tempo with the child's breathing rate and to slowly change tempo in order to match a relaxed breathing rate. Key words and phrases can be marked out by changing the voice tone, by pausing before or after the word or phrase, by clearing the throat, by tapping lightly on the desk or by any other action that is somewhat out of context with the present state of awareness.

Through careful observation, limited expectations and a slow pace, the child and youth care professional can assist the most impulsive, overactive child to learn to slow down and to relax.

## Relaxation, Imagery, and Guided Fantasy with the Atypical Child

### The Overly Active Child

Children experiencing attention problems must initially have limited goals but, with the long-term expectation that they will be able to slow themselves down as effectively as their peers are able to. Since these individuals tend to be very active; the child and youth care professional should meet them at this state. Providing exercises that incorporate music and movement allows the child to move but gives the child and youth care professional some control over this movement. Chapter Fifteen (Art, Drama, Music, and Movement) will be of assistance in generating ideas to help the child relax. The tempo of the music and the texture of the music can slowly be softened thus, slowing down the overactive child. Eventually, the child can be asked to sit and to move only his/her hands to the music and then to lie down moving either hands or legs to music. Movement is slowly decreased to the point where the child is lying or sitting and merely imagining that s/he is moving to the music. Slow steps with as many aids as possible allow children to gain more self-control over their movements. Children with attention and activity level difficulties require physical aids and cues to assist them to relax. A back rub slowly reduced to a hand on their shoulder, reduced to periodic touching can greatly assist these children. Often the child can identify what other aids may be needed in order to slow down and to concentrate. A stuffed animal, a blanket, a picture, a mandala, or a favourite object can often assist in helping them to relax. Exercises such as Magic Button, Affirmations and Reframing, included at the end of this chapter, as well as the centering and grounding activities, are particularly useful for children with these types of problems. Note that these children often have a weak sense of self-worth; therefore, patience and limited expectations will allow them to make progress. Also, any activity that increases their sense of self will assist in this and other areas of their lives.

### The Impulsive Child

Children with poor impulse control can be assisted in much the same way as the overactive child; however, these children can often relax and use imagery much more effectively. Imagery and guided fantasy exercises that emphasize thinking before acting, checking with your feelings before acting, slowing down and holding on to emotions can be most useful. The Imaginary Doctor exercise, in the activity section of Chapter Twelve, can be used to encourage the child to contact their inner wisdom to give them clues to controlling impulsive behavior. Heroes/Heroines, included in this chapter, can be used to help the child gain control by internalizing the strengths of others. Magic Buttons and Affirmations, also included in this chapter, can assist this type of child in gaining more impulse control. Grounding, centering and relaxation exercises also add to this child's ability to be less impulsive.

### The Lethargic and Poorly Motivated Child

Imagery, affirmations, and external centering help these children to access their creativity in order to better motivate and activate themselves. Children experiencing these types of difficulties often experience a negative self-talk, that negative internal voice that tells them that they are bad. This experience often causes them to get stuck in unpleasent emotions or in a mild depression and thus they become lethargic or poorly motivated. The negative self-talk causes the child to feel upset which promotes more negative self-talk. These two strategies feed on one another and form a cooperative that causes chronic problems. Visual and auditory activities can take these children out of this self-destructive thought process. Mobilization helps to promote motivation; therefore, creative movement, art, and large muscle activities help to get children motivated. These children are often skilled at visual imagery; however, many times these images are non-supportive and it becomes a task of changing those negative images to positive images. Magic Buttons, Grounding, and Heroes/Heroines included in the activity section are useful exercises for working with children who are passive. Many of these children can learn to meditate and increase their energy through centering exercises.

### The Fearful Child

The most important factor in working with children who are fearful is to understand clearly what fears are normal for their age or developmental stage. Children from toddlers to middle childhood often experience fearful stages as part of normal development. Fear is not to be seen as an aspect to eliminate from the child's life. It is often very wise to be fearful. A supportive and flexible environment helps considerably to allow children to express and to explore their fears. Art and drama are excellent medicines to use in the expression and in the exploration of fears. Relaxation and centering allow the child to gain some control over intense fear responses. Grounding exercises help the fearful child to feel more connected to and supported by his/her environment. The exercises Affirmations and Heroes/Heroines, in this chapter, help the child to gain strength internally which assists in stabilization. The Dream Arm exercise, also included in this chapter, can be an excellent technique for the child and youth care professional to add affirming messages to the child's internal processes. The Imaginary Doctor exercise, found in Chapter Twelve, can stimulate the child to search for alternate strategies of expressing their fears. Positive imagery and the exercise, Magic Buttons, give the child added support in adjusting to fearful situations. Also, consult Chapter Twelve for useful strategies for expressing fear. There are a wide variety of ways to allow children to understand, to appreciate, and to live comfortably with their fears.

### The Aggressive Child

Aggressive children, much like overactive children, will need to start with a higher level of activity in their relaxation exercises in order to provide them with the several small steps that prepare them for grounding, centering, and guided fantasy exercises. Grounding and centering give the aggressive child a sense of self-control. Art, drama, and creative movement allow for creative outlets of emotion. The aggressive or angry child is often reacting to fear, sorrow, or abandonment which is expressed through anger. The exercises, Affirmations and Magic Buttons, included in the activity section, provide children with alternatives to expressing these emotions rather than masking them with anger and violence. The Imaginary Doctor exercise in Chapter Twelve, as well as the Heroes/Heroines exercise from this chapter, can provide an added sense of personal strength and healthy role models to help them deal with their emotions. Also, consult Chapter Twelve for productive ways of expressing anger. Aggression and violence are very complex issues and a multi-dimensional approach to the problem is often most effective.

### Lying and Stealing Behaviors

Lying and stealing often reflect a child's feelings of disconnection with their father figure. Exploring his/her relationship with father figures often provides clues as to how to treat the behavior. The exercise, Heroes/

Heroines, can often be useful in treating this type of problem, in that it can provide the child with a wide variety of alternative behaviors that will help to achieve a sense of belonging. These behaviors can be symptomatic of other underlying issues for the child. Centering and grounding help the child to feel more in control and more balanced. Imagery and affirmations can often assist the child to resist the temptation to lie or to steal and can provide an alternative for more appropriate behaviour. A program to help children with problems in these areas needs to be of a multi-dimensional perspective.

**A mind never thinks without a mental picture.**

**ARISTOTLE**

## Activities

### ♦ SPECIAL PLACE

- Ask the group to lie or sit in a comfortable position and to slowly relax themselves. Then begin: As you find yourself slowing down
- slowing down your thoughts
- you can begin to prepare yourself
- to travel in your mind to a special place;
- it can be an imaginary place or a real place but
- it's a place that makes you feel good, safe, and confident.
- Look around and explore your surroundings.
- Are there colors or is it black and white?
- Notice what is moving
- and what is staying still?
- Explore your special place by looking all around you.
- Listen,
- what sounds do you hear in your special place?
- Are there voices, or is it quiet?.
- What are you saying to yourself?
- If you have not already done so, step into the picture you have imagined and become you in your special place.
- What does it feel like to be in your special place?
- Enjoy all the positive feelings associated with your special place.
- Take a last look around and know that you can return to this place whenever you wish.
- Now, slowly taking all the time you need, return your thoughts to this place in the here and now.

## ♦ THE DREAM ARM

This is a good exercise to begin when starting to do relaxation. It is fun, and non-threatening and encourages internalization. It also works well as a quiet activity in other areas of programming.

Have the group pair up. Ask for a volunteer or choose the person who has paired up with you and demonstrate for the group. The person can either stand or sit. Ask that person to think of a favorite television show, preferably a half-hour program. Some children prefer a cartoon. When s/he has chosen, ask him/her to close his/her eyes, raise an arm up over the head, and pretend to be watching the program. As the program progresses, this person should lower the arm slowly. The program will be over when his/her arm has come back down. As the person lowers the arm, stop it with your hand at intervals and say, "It is time for a commercial," and add some positive comment for the future, e.g., "Won't you be surprised when you wake up tomorrow and feel rested and alert," or "Won't you be surprised when you leave here at how much you understood and uncovered about yourself." Only when the person's arm is down, do you ask that the eyes open.

## ♦ RELAXATION ONE

This is a good exercise to begin formal relaxation techniques. It can also be incorporated into guided fantasy, yoga, grounding, and centering exercises. It is also useful as a cool-down for gym programs.

Ask the group members to sit or lie down and to make themselves comfortable. Explain to the group the importance of quiet in this exercise. Proceed with the following dialogue:

- Close your eyes and get ready for a journey through your body.
- We will begin at your feet.
- Tighten all the muscles in your feet.
- Now, relax them.
- Tighten all the muscles in your legs.
- Now, relax them.
- Tighten all the muscles in your mid-section:
- your stomach
- your chest
- your buttocks
- and your back.
- Now relax them.
- Take a deep breath and let it out.

- Now, tighten all the muscles in your arms and neck.
- Relax.
- Now your face,
- tighten all the muscles in your face.
- And relax.
- Think back to one good thing that has happened in the past hour (or whatever the length of group time).
- Now slowly begin to wake up your bodies.
- When you feel ready, open your eyes and focus your attention on me.

Suggestions: Speak slowly in monotone. Allow children to squirm a bit at first. Some will be unable to relax at first. There is no need to pressure them; however, re-emphasize the importance of quiet in this exercise. It is important to allow the group time to re-orient themselves after this exercise. Discourage them from getting up right away.

## ♦ RELAXATION TWO

This is a little more detailed and demanding of the participants than Relaxation One. It is useful in a number of settings and it also works well with adults. Proceed as follows:

- Find yourself a space on the floor and lie down on your back.
- Wiggle around a bit until you feel comfortable.
- Uncross your legs and place your hands down beside you.
- Spread your legs apart a few inches.
- Let your eyes close when they are ready and feel them relax in the darkness.
- Let your body begin to settle down one part at a time.
- Let your hair . . . scalp . . . and head . . . relax.
- Now your face muscles . . . your jaw, and your neck.
- Bit by bit your body is allowing itself to relax.
- Relax your shoulders . . . arms . . . wrists . . . and hands.
- Now relax your chest . . . your stomach . . . your buttocks . . . your legs . . . your knees . . . your ankles . . . and your feet.
- Allow your breath to flow up from your toes to the top of your head to relax your muscles . . . organs . . . bones . . . blood vessels . . . tendons . . . and skin.
- Take in a deep breath, allow your chest to rise and your lungs to be completely filled with air.
- Follow the air from outside in through your nose, down your windpipe, and into your lungs.

- Take a deep breathe counting as the air comes in: one . . . two . . . three . . . four . . . five . . . and six. . . . let the air out making a hissing sound and counting one . . . two . . . three . . . four . . . five . . . six . . . seven . . . and eight . . . (Repeat this breathing for five breaths).
- As you breath deeper and deeper you feel physically weaker and weaker as your muscles completely let go.
- It's a good thing to relax your muscles to give them a short rest during the day.
- You can feel relaxed when you choose by breathing in deeply and concentrating on your breathing.
- In a few minutes . . . I will ask you to come back to the room.
- Until then . . . enjoy your relaxed feeling.
- When I count from seven to eleven you will wake your body up and come back to the room.
- seven . . . eight . . . nine . . . ten . . . and eleven.

## ♦ PHYSICAL CENTER

This is a good exercise for children to explore their physical self. It can be most useful when repeated daily or at regular intervals to allow the children to center themselves. Begin with one of the relaxation exercises.

- Now that you are relaxed, I want you to attend to your breathing.
- Lungs are shaped like a pear . . . smaller at the top and wider at the bottom . . . When we breathe into the bottom of our lungs, a deep breath . . . we put more air into our lungs . . . The air in our lungs goes into our blood system and refreshes our body.
- Breathe deeply into your lungs and allow your body to be energized.
- By breathing slowly, you can fill your lungs up with air and then let all of the air out.
- There is a spot just below your navel which is the center of your body . . . Imagine now as you breathe deeply that you are sending the energy to this spot.
- Breathe into your center and feel the energy rise.
- Once you have located the center and are able to send the energy from areas of the body that to the center you may relax and enjoy that feeling.
- Draw your attention to the center of your body and feel the different organs and parts of the body are in sync with one another.
- You can choose to feel relaxed and centered whenever you desire.
- All you need to do is to remember the feelings and visions and voices from today and find yourself thinking much the same as you are now.

♦ Taking enough time to understand what is necessary for you . . . I want the group to slowly bring their attention . . . back to the room . . . and when you are back . . . show me your elbow.

## ♦ EXTERNAL CENTERING

This exercise is sometimes useful for the distractable child who is having difficulties with the relaxation or centering process. It can also work well with the child who has a short attention span.

♦ Walk around the area (room, outdoors, gym, etc.) and explore the room using all of your senses. Use your eyes to notice the entire area and also the small details. Remember this is a quiet exercise. There is to be no talking.
♦ Notice the people . . . the color . . . and the movement around you.
♦ Use your ears to record all the sounds within the area.
♦ Listen to even the smallest and to the weakest sound.
♦ Listen to any changes in the sounds.
♦ Now feel your feet as they touch the ground, feel the temperature of your skin . . . feel the textures . . . the shapes of the objects . . . and the people around you.
♦ Feel the muscles in your body . . . as you move about.
♦ Breathe in . . . and smell all of the different smells around you . . . the faint ones . . . and the stronger ones.
♦ Note the different tastes in your mouth.
♦ Your mouth can be dry and still there can be a taste.
♦ Spend a few more minutes exploring the world around you.
♦ Now slowly return to the room.

## ♦ SENSORY CENTERING

This exercise allows the child to center on the different sensory experiences. It is useful to help distractable and impulsive children center in on things in a light and non-threatening atmosphere.

♦ Now that you are feeling relaxed, I would like you to imagine that you can see in your mind's eye, some of the people and things that make you feel happy.
♦ Focus in clearly and make the pictures as colorful as you like.
♦ Now think of a funny face, one you have never seen before.
♦ Listen to any voices or laughter inside of you . . . Do not be surprised if you hear bells or singers.

- Can you make up a special sound that only you can hear inside of your head?
- Breathe in deeply and imagine that you can feel all of the emotions that you want to.
- Remember a time when someone touched you in a special way and it felt good.
- Imagine what a moon rock feels like.
- Think about the last time you tasted a delicious treat.
- Allow yourself to remember and almost taste that treat again.
- Breathe in through your nostrils and be aware of any smells that you can imagine.
- Remember pleasant smells that bring back pleasant memories.
- Take a deep breath and listen for more pictures, smells, or tastes.
- Take a moment to remember them and then slowly come back to this place.
- Raise your hands when you can see my face.

## ♦ GROUNDING EXERCISE

This is also an excellent exercise for distractable, impulsive children. It allows them to feel, however fleeting, their first experiences of being grounded and firmly rooted. This exercise needs to be repeated several times in order for some children to get the full benefit of it.

- In order for us to feel more solid and connected with the universe, concentration is helpful. For a short time I would like you to imagine yourself as a tree, a flower, a shrub, or any living plant that gives you a good feeling.
- Experience for a moment, as you listen to the sounds, a feeling for what it's like to enjoy life as a living plant. Concentration can be done with either the eyes opened or closed. As you stand there feeling your body responding, imagine the different parts of the plant.
- Your feet now planted on the ground, imagine you have roots going deep down into the earth. A plant has an entire network of roots and rootlets which nourish the plant. Imagine how firmly the deep roots create a sound grip on the earth . . . such a firm hold that even the strongest wind or the hardest rain cannot shake.
- Feel the energy flow from the earth up the root ends into the plant.
- Listen for any messages being sent up from the earth and notice how firmly planted your plant is.

- If it feels comfortable, reach your arms up as the branches, leaves, stems, and buds of a plant would do in order to obtain energy from the sun and air.
- Your arms in the air can receive energy from the atmosphere that flows to the ends of the roots allowing the plant to feel as if it were one unit . . . one solid flexible unit.
- The sweet smell of vegetation can bring back memories that can be enjoyed.
- You can remember whenever you choose, to feel grounded and one with the earth. Stand as you are standing now or any way that feels comfortable.
- Remember how a plant feels . . . how it looks . . . what sounds it hears, and talk to yourself about these things.
- Soon you will feel very much part of the earth you are standing on. This calm feeling may help you whenever you wish.
- In the morning as the young plant awakens to the warmth of the sun . . . feeling well-rested . . . so you may become this way by slowly noticing the others and listening for the sounds of the room around you.
- Stop long enough to remember for your own benefit the feeling of being firmly grounded.
- When it feels right, I want you to slowly return your attention to this place where I am.

## ♦ CLEANSING

This exercise can be used for any of the internal organs or for the whole body. It relaxes and eases stress in specific areas and sets up a series of physiological reactions.

- Sitting there, feeling comfortable, and relaxed . . . I want you to prepare yourself to travel inside your body . . . inside to the area we call your (lungs, mind, heart, muscles, etc.).
- Travel to that place right now.
- Imagine that part of you being cleansed . . . and soothed . . . and comforted . . . and relaxed.
- Send a message to your system to clean and repair that part of you so it's working perfectly.
- See that part of you and thank it for being such a good part . . . such a useful part . . . such an important part.
- Imagine it being slowly and lovingly cleaned and repaired . . . soothed, and relaxed.
- When the time feels right, slowly return your attention back to this room.

**Variations:**
The children can be asked to image themselves as tiny enough to travel inside their bodies as characters such as tiny men, women, or imaginary characters that can be called on to do the cleaning. For more in-depth imagery, the child and youth care professional can seek medical assistance and advice as to how to best word this fantasy to fit each particular child, especially those with medical problems.

## ♦ HEROES/HEROINES

This exercise invites the child to model and take on the positive attributes they see in their role models. Children can be encouraged to emulate aspects of these characters and to incorporate their positive characteristics into their own individual personalities and characters.

Begin by relaxing the group and the repeat the following:

- Now that you are feeling relaxed and comfortable . . . soothed and quiet,
- I want you to take some time to think about . . . a hero or heroine of yours, a character whom you would most want to be like. . . . It can be any character you wish, imaginary or real.
- Take some time, all the time you need to think of this character.
- If you have not already done so, imagine that you can see that person in your imagination.
- How do they look? . . . Make the picture as clear and as colourful as you wish.
- Are there any sounds in this picture?
- How is your hero feeling?
- What is it you most like about this character?
- Imagine that your hero is giving you this talent.
- Now imagine that you are your hero or heroine.
- Step into the picture and become that person.
- Imagine you are taking on the strengths and positive abilities of your hero/heroine.
- Feel yourself becoming like that person.
- Now go back to being yourself, except take with you those parts or abilities of your hero or heroine that you most admire.
- Take some time to feel yourself changing . . . slowly, not all at once . . . but little by little, day by day, develop your abilities to match your character.
- Now picture your hero or heroine again . . . Thank that person for helping you.

- Ask if you can visit with him/her again in your imagination.
- Whenever you want to be more like your hero or heroine you can remember this exercise.
- In a minute I will ask you to return to the room.
- Take the last few moments to be with your hero or heroine.
- Now slowly return your thoughts to this room.

## ♦ MAGIC BUTTONS

This is a more advanced exercise and is more beneficial after children have mastered relaxation. This is a deep relaxation exercise and should be preceded by Relaxation One or Relaxation Two. This exercise uses confidence as the desired attribute; however, any feeling, talent, or attribute can be inserted to replace the word **CONFIDENT.**

- Find a relaxed and comfortable position and let your mind drift off to a very peaceful and contented time for you.
- Notice your surroundings and arrange them in any way that you wish until you begin to feel the small muscles in your face and your jaw let go and relax.
- Now that your muscles are relaxing, I would like you to think of someone who you consider to be very **CONFIDENT.**
- Picture how this person looks, sounds, and feels. Make that picture with those sounds and feelings as clear as it needs to be for you to appreciate this person for his or her **CONFIDENCE.**
- Imagine you are that person and can feel his/her confidence.
- When you can feel the confidence in you press firmly one of your knuckles. This will be your confidence button.
- Each time throughout this exercise when you feel confident, press your confidence button in order to make it stronger.
- Take another look at this person and notice any detail that you may have missed.
- Listen closely to the sound of your person's voice and be aware of its **CONFIDENT** sound. You may wish to talk to yourself quietly about the sound and remark on its **CONFIDENT** tone.
- Be aware of how it might feel to possess the degree of **CONFIDENCE** that you feel flowing from this person.
- Be aware of times in your life when you felt **CONFIDENT.**

**Variation:** This exercise can be used using the same button to stack a number of feelings, talents, or attributes. Repeat the exercise according to the desired number of feelings, talents, or attributes you wish to instill in the child and use the same position on the body, e.g., the knuckle, to represent each talent, etc. Therefore when the child stimulates that part of the body they will get a memory of each talent, etc.

## ♦ AFFIRMATIONS

This exercise follows a similar format as Magic Buttons. It is preceded by a relaxation exercise, it eliminates the use of the button concept, and relies on the individual's experience.

This exercise uses courage as the desired attribute; however, any feeling, talent, or attribute can be inserted to replace the word **COURAGE**.

- Allow your mind to drift to a time when you felt **COURAGEOUS.**
- Be aware of how you looked . . . how you sounded . . . and how your body felt.
- As you are experiencing this feeling say to yourself . . . "I am strong and courageous and can handle any situation."
- Now imagine a person whom you believe to be **COURAGEOUS** and be aware of any similarities between you and that person.
- Say to yourself, "I am strong and courageous just like ______."
- Each time in the future when **COURAGE** is necessary and beneficial, a conscious and/or unconscious recollection of that person and your own ability to be **COURAGEOUS** will assist you to a positive outcome.
- Take time now to appreciate yourself and that person and then orient yourself slowly back to the present.

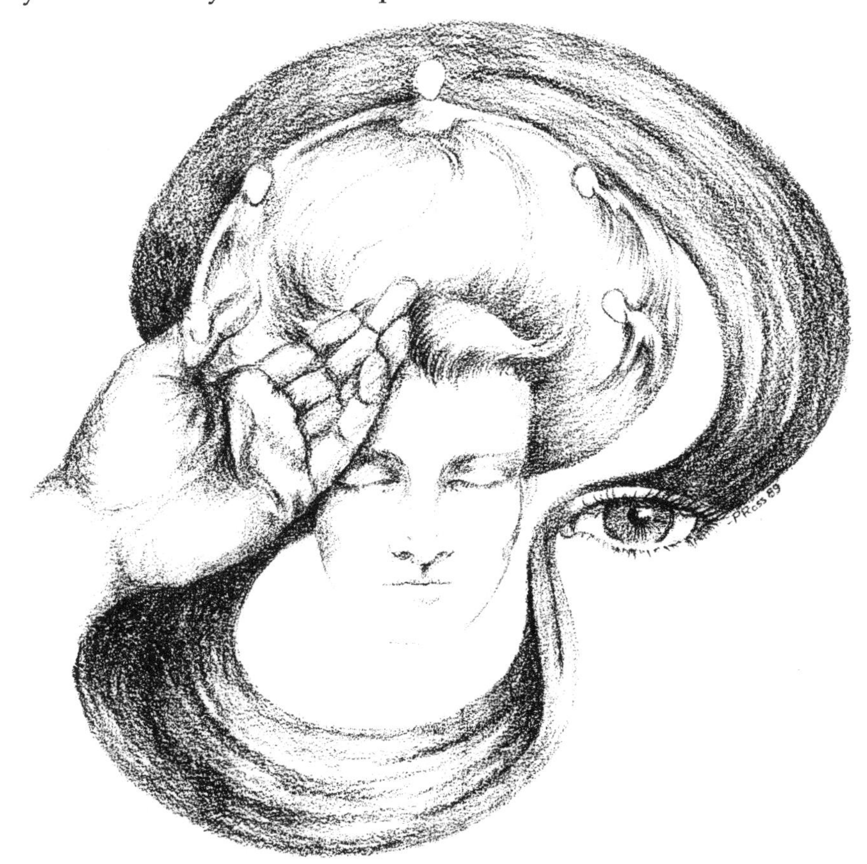

## Bibliography for RELAXATION, IMAGERY, AND GUIDED FANTASY

Beary, J. (1974). A simple psychophysiologic technique which elicits the hypometabolic changes of the relaxation response. *Psychosomatic Medicine, 36*, 119–126.

Elkind, D. (1988). *The hurried child.* Toronto: Addison-Wesley.

Hendricks, G., & Wills, R. (1975). *The centering book.* Englewood Cliffs, NJ: Prentice-Hall.

Hendricks, G., & Roberts, T. (1977). *The second centering book.* Englewood Cliffs, NJ: Prentice-Hall.

Murdock, M. (1987). *Spinning inward: Using guided imagery with children for learning, creativity, and relaxation.* Boston, MA: Shambhala.

Samuels, M., & Samuels, N. (1975). *Seeing with the mind's eye.* New York: Random House.

CHAPTER FOURTEEN

# STORYTELLING

Brownie, my father's working buddy, would always send us home a treat in Dad's lunch box. An apple, a pear, a sandwich, a banana, and even the occasional Molly'O bar was presented to us as "a treat from Brownie." Dad would often tell us stories about Brownie, about his life, his family, the happy times, and the unhappy times in his life. Brownie would make us laugh with his jokes and the with funny situations that he found himself in. Brownie would make us sad and sometimes tears would well up in our eyes, like the time when Dad told us that Brownie's dog, Max, died, or the time Brownie had to go to the hospital for a serious operation. We all loved Brownie very much and looked forward to Dad's stories each night. We never did meet Brownie, but we assumed that he got older and so did we and the stories about him lessened mainly because we were busy growing up and we spent less time with Dad.

It was not until shortly after my father's death that I realized that Brownie was my father and that his stories were ways of communicating his own life experiences, his lessons, his morals, and his ideas to us. He communicated these messages in a way that we could easily understand and in a way that we could internalize what was important to him in life. His stories allowed us to deal with events in our lives that were difficult to talk about. Brownie talked to us from a deep sense of love and understanding.

> **Inasmuch as the use of metaphor as a means of communication has been widespread throughout recorded history, we must assume that there are distinct advantages to delivering messages in metaphorical form.**
>
> **PHILIP BARKER**

The birth of the story runs concurrent with the beginning of humankind's ability to communicate with signs and movements. Since that early beginning in human history to the present date, stories have been an integral part of human existence. The faded markings on cave walls are testimony to our need to recreate the past and to tell stories of possible future exploits. Over the centuries, these chronicles have taken on many forms of expression. In the beginning, most of our stories were told to explain our existence, to give meaning to life's mysteries, or to justify our actions. Other stories were meant purely for entertainment, sometimes giving us a chance to laugh at our follies; others were meant to instruct and to point the way to a useful and meaningful life.

The forms that stories took over the centuries were as varied as their tellers. Some were pictorial accounts etched on stone, wood, cloth, metal, and later, on paper. Most were told from memory and passed on down through the generations. Stories were told in rhyme, or in verse and, sometimes were composed to a tune meant to be sung. Others were told in the form of a riddle asking the listener to unfold the mystery. Tales were acted out in mime at first and, later, the actors were given lines to read. Stories were written out by hand and, later, typed; pictures were added to give them more life. Centuries later, these pictures began to move on a screen and, still later, these moving pictures were given sound.

Stories have been told in every language and in every corner of the globe. From the pictographic stories on the walls of caves to the tales told on the space shuttles and space stations, humans give in to a relentless urge to communicate with their world.

A knowledge of a variety of types and styles of stories provides child and youth care professionals with countless opportunities to communicate, to teach, and to heal the children in their care. Storytelling has many uses in recreational programming for children and youth. Stories can be told to entertain, to build rapport, to create closeness, to change the mood, to build self-esteem, to desensitize children to fear and to other feelings, to express, feel and understand their emotions, to teach, to communicate, to motivate, to redefine problems in a creative way, to provide alternative solutions, and also to stimulate the imagination of children in order for them to make sense and purpose out of their worlds.

## ♦ Exercise 14:1

- ♦ Place yourself in a relaxed posture, and slowly count backwards from ten to one; with each number you will find your muscles and skin relaxing deeper and deeper. Begin . . . 10 . . . 9 . . . 8 . . . 7 . . . with each breath your body and mind slow down and relax . . . 6 . . . 5 . . . 4 . . . 3 . . . eyelids are getting heavy . . . 2 . . . and 1 . . .
- ♦ Drift back to a happy time in your childhood and recall the storytellers and the stories that were told to you as you grew to adulthood.
- ♦ Listen to one or two of those stories now, but hear them with the ears of an adult.
- ♦ What wisdom do you hear in the storyline?
- ♦ Were there any stories that you wanted to hear over and over again?
- ♦ Who was the best storyteller, and how can you utilize their style or ability to model efficiency in your storytelling?
- ♦ Take ninety seconds to assimilate your learning and, when you finish, bring yourself back into the space where you began this exercise, carrying with you new knowledge and experience.

## Uses of Storytelling

### Entertainment

This is a primary goal for most storytellers. Children love to hear stories told to them and the more that these are dramatized, the more they enjoy them. Children are never very far from the world of make believe, and a skilled storyteller can allow them to explore this realm and to be entertained by a story line. Child and youth care professionals with five or six stories known by memory can entertain a group of children and these can be used strategically at times when there is a danger that idle time may not be used constructively.

### Building Rapport

Storytelling entertains and, thus, promotes positive feelings between the storyteller and the audience. They share the experience of the story and, in this sharing, rapport is developed and strengthened. Children feel more at ease because of the less threatening aspect of this type of communication. When children are feeling anxious or unsure of the child and youth care professional or the situation that they are in, a well-chosen story can relieve some of the anxiety and can strengthen the relationship between storyteller and audience.

### Creating Intimacy

The entertaining and rapport-building qualities of storytelling often create an intimacy between the narrator and the audience. There is a communion of the adventure, the emotion, and the life of the characters that creates a bond between the storyteller and audience. This union can develop into a sense of closeness or intimacy which strengthens the relationships between child and youth care professionals and the children in their care.

### Changing Moods

The magic created by the storyteller and the story line has the power to change the gloom of a group of teenagers into laughter or relaxation. It can motivate an apprehensive classroom to try harder; or, it can calm down a room full of boisterous ten year-olds. When the child and youth care professional selects the appropriate story, s/he has the opportunity to creatively change the prevailing mood and to enhance the situation by creating more opportunities for success.

### Building Self-Esteem

Storytelling has the power to strengthen self-esteem. Stories can compliment and praise an individual or a group by paralleling their lives or the lives of the listeners with those of the characters. As well, rapport building, intimacy, and positive interactions between the storyteller and the audience automatically strengthen the self-esteem of the participants.

The child and youth care professional can actively select and recount stories that are specifically geared to strengthen the self-esteem of the audience.

### Desensitizing

When children are introduced or confronted with their fears, anxieties, and apprehensions by way of identifying with a character(s) in a story, they are able to distance themselves from the stress, and to look at the problem with more objectivity. Bruno Bettelheim, in his book, *The Uses of Enchantment*, stresses the quality of storytelling that allows the child to experience these uncomfortable emotions; and so, they become more comfortable with them (Bettelheim, 1977).

### Emotional Release

Stories told that concern death and dying can provide the grieving child with a vehicle with which to express emotions. Scary stories give ventilation to many of a child's unexpressed fears. Stories told of pain and destruction often open up these feelings in their listeners, allowing them to identify and to release their feelings within the context of the story. The cathartic effect that stories have on their listeners can be utilized by the child and youth care professional in order to give children an appropriate way in which to express their emotions.

### Teaching

Stories can be used to explain and to communicate any one or a variety of skills, ideas, concepts, morals, and points specific to learning. They can be used to introduce new material or to review topics already discussed. Stories can provide step-by-step instructions on how to acquire new skills. Child and youth care professionals, in their role as educators, can make use of storytelling to enhance the learning process for the children in their care.

### Communicating Indirectly

Inherent in storytelling is the ability to communicate indirectly to the listener. The fact that the storyteller is, in most cases, telling a story about something that happened to someone or something else, distances the audience enough so that listeners are able to decide, both consciously and unconsciously, how certain aspects of the story relate to their life situation. Therefore, a child can listen to the story and decide: that character is exactly like me; that part of the character's experience, moods, etc. are similar to mine; or the story is about someone else and it does not apply to me at all.

This ambiguous aspect of the story allows the child and youth care professional to communicate with the child about a topic or an event that is difficult for the child to talk about in a direct conversation. There are many situations where it is more important to discuss topics indirectly in order not to embarrass the child, to traumatize the child, to cause the child to lose face, or to confuse the child. Stories that speak metaphorically to the child often are more successful in inviting change than more direct forms of communication. As a rule, children are far less resistant to the language of metaphor than they are to direct conversation. Stories can be used most effectively in situations where other strategies have proven unsuccessful.

### Redefining Problems

When children are communicated to by means of a story, they will often project their problems on to the characters in the story. This not only allows them to distance themselves; it redefines the problem for them in the eyes, ears, and emotions of the story's characters. This provides children with the opportunity to see their problems in a new way.

### Providing Alternatives/Solutions

When children are presented with solutions to their problems in a metaphorical fashion, solutions will often come through identification with the character(s). The child is free to utilize the strategy that the character in the story used, or the child can adapt a strategy that is better suited to his/her situation. The more solutions presented, the more alternatives there are to solving the problem. Depending on the developmental level of the child, s/he can be presented with as many alternate solutions as s/he can appreciate in order to make a decision based on the best choice.

### Stimulating Unconscious Search

Stories that offer no solutions to the character's problems, for example, an open-ended story, that the child participates in by completing it, requires the child to search his/her unconscious mind/imagination for a solution. Since the child is searching for solutions for someone else, there may be more creativity in the search. The solutions that are provided for the character(s) will be a clue or a complete strategy that the child may choose to implement in his/her life. This exercise empowers the child and shows that s/he is often his/her own best resource.

## Story Selection

In the beginning, it is always best to familiarize yourself with the tried and true tales and legends that have stood the test of time. Fairy tales by the

Brothers Grimm, Hans Christian Andersen, and Scheherazade of the Arabian Nights are centuries old and are still very popular today. Many of these stories have been rewritten to appeal to the modern-day audience; however, in their retranslation, much of their impact and diversity is eliminated. Bruno Bettelheim, in *The Uses of Enchantment* (1977), points this out in relation to the removal of frightening and violent episodes or scenes in the rewriting of the Grimm Brothers' fairy tales. When these scenes are removed, children are denied the opportunity to deal with their content and their lessons or to familiarize themselves with how it feels for others and themselves in these situations. They are also denied the chance to interpret the lessons for themselves in order to gain insight from the characters and their behaviors, thoughts, and feelings. It is this exposure to these scenes that allows the child to come to grips with his/her fear, dread, loneliness, anger, and so on; therefore, it is best to learn the story in its original form or as close to the original form as possible. Other good sources of material are in the myths, legends, and folk tales of various cultures. These stories provide endless opportunities for the child and youth care professional to adopt or adapt their story lines, and to present them to the children in a way that they can best benefit from their messages. The storyteller should be familiar with as many of these stories as possible as a beginning step to using metaphor as a way of enhancing the lives of children and youth.

A next step towards the use of story is to learn the intent of the story line of these classic tales. This requires the child and youth care professional to study and to discuss with other professionals, the essential lessons communicated by a particular legend, myth, or tale. Storytellers need to be aware of the more unconscious, symbolic, and subtle meanings of the story as well, in order to be most effective in communicating their message.

## ♦ Exercise 14:2

- Select a popular myth, legend, or fairy tale.
- Read the story from beginning to end twice, three times if it is unfamiliar to you.
- Draw sketches of its main characters, its symbols, and key scenes in the story line.
- Conduct a guided fantasy and, in your imagination, become one of the characters in the story.
- What lessons do you learn or teach in the story?
- Is there a moral to this story?

- If so, write it down.
- Read over the list "Uses of Storytelling" and apply your story to the list. How many uses can you identify in this story?
- Read the story again. How would your presentation of this story to a group of six-year-olds differ from a presentation to a group of sixteen-year-olds?

When selecting a story, it is always useful to decide, "What message or effect do I want this to convey?" There are several good sources of children's books; to list them all would take up a great deal of time and space. Librarians, school teachers, early childhood educators, child and youth care workers, instructors, and colleagues are good resources for effective children's metaphors and stories. Some research and plenty of reading is required until you find one that suits your specific needs. When you have located one of special significance, memorize it, buy it, or put it in point form in your diary because it will prove useful in many situations. The most successful storytellers will spend the bulk of their time researching and learning specific stories; the telling is usually the easiest and most enjoyable part.

Once you have chosen a suitable story that conveys the necessary message(s), and once you know the story line well, it is time to add the finishing touches to your creation. This requires the storyteller to contact the creative artist within, and to exercise these abilities in order to enhance the presentation of the story.

A story comes alive in the imagination of the audience when the storyteller uses his/her voice and body, and the story content to breathe life into the words, and to create the images, sounds, and emotions that represent the experience that the words of the story intend to convey.

## The Voice

Inflection, which is the change in pitch or loudness of the voice and tonation, which is the changing of the texture or sound of the voice, can make the words thunder, whistle in the wind, tremble with fear, shine like the stars, or float like a feather. Inflection and tonation can mark out key words and phrases that emphasize certain lessons, morals, or ideas. They can calm or they can arouse, depending on the storyteller's wishes. Tempo, the rate of speed in which you speak, also conveys meaning. Tempo can make words drag, move slowly, dance, run quickly, or flash like lightening. Tempo can be used to enhance the calming effect of the story, or to mark out certain words or phrases. It can be rhythmic or spastic, depending upon the storyteller's wishes. The combination of all of these qualities bring life and wonder to the story's tale.

## ♦ Exercise 14:3

- You will need a tape recorder and a book of poetry for this exercise.
- Relax yourself by using a favourite technique or one from the chapter on relaxation.
- Listen to the voices of others within your head. What are they saying?
- Listen to your own internal voice. What is it saying?
- Be aware how the use of inflection and tempo gets the message across.
- Now listen in your mind to one or both of your parents' voices.
- How do they use inflection to convey emotion?
- Listen to the words of a favourite song, and be aware of how the singer conveys the song's message, the song's emotion.
- Allow yourself to hear other voices from the past.
- How does the sender use tempo and inflection in order to convey meaning?
- Slowly come back to the room and maintain the memory of the communication styles that you have learned from in your lifetime.
- Now open your book of poetry.
- Read through a poem several times in order to analyze the meaning of the words and the message of the poem.
- Turn on your tape recorder and read the poem using tempo, inflection, and pauses in order to underscore the poem's meaning.
- Play back your reading of the poem and critique it.
- Work on this piece until it sounds the way that you feel it was intended to sound.
- Try this technique with several other poems; it will increase your ability to use your voice as an instrument of emotion, sensation, imagery, and meaning.

## The Body

Gestures, positioning, and movement express emotion and convey meaning just as words do. A whole story can be told non-verbally through mime. Most of the communication between communicators is non-verbal. The use of the body can enhance the story's clarity and the intended message or moral.

Gestures, the use of movement of the extremities to express meaning, are a dramatic tool that can liven up the story. The storyteller shows size, shape, re-enacts a character's gestures or exaggerates them, shows direction, shows actions like reaching, pulling, climbing, kicking, etc. Movement can beckon, quiet, scold, and threaten. Gestures can also be used as an overt or covert cue for the listener to pay attention to a specific word or phrase in order to underscore its meaning. An overt gesture could be pointing with the arm and hand; a covert gesture could be a subtle stroke of the chin. These gestures hold attention and mark out the key learning or healing elements of the story.

Facial gestures and eye contact convey a myriad of meanings and are often used unconsciously by the storyteller. A common practice for storytellers is to tell their story in front of a mirror in order to be aware of their facial expressions and as a way to improve their ability to express meaning.

The positioning of the body in space, and the movement of the body through space, can also have an effect on the communication process. The position of the storyteller in respect to the audience at any time during the delivery of the story has an effect on the audience's perception. Each time the storyteller changes body posture in relation to the different members of the audience (as in sitting facing the audience, beside the audience, in back of the audience, etc.), s/he changes the meaning of the story and the focal point of the experience. The changing of body posture and position can be choreographed in order to make the story more entertaining and more effective in terms of communication. The storyteller/child and youth care professional must experiment in order to decide how each story should be dramatized. Props can be used by the storyteller for added effects or can be used by the group in the presentation of the story. Puppets, flannel boards, picture books, and artwork can all be used as communicators. Some storytellers use no props and very little dramatization, while others use props and dramatization frequently. The child and youth care professional can experiment and decide which stories can be more effective with the use of the body and non-verbal communication.

## ♦ Exercise 14:4

- Decide on a favourite children's story, fairy tale or nursery rhyme.
- Choose a comfortable position and close your eyes.
- Run the story through in your mind imagining that the sound is off and that all you read is body language.
- Select a character that you would like to focus on.
- Watch the character's non-verbal language.
- Take on some of the body postures of this character.
- If there is room, move around like the character does.
- Add the gestures, facial expressions and any other forms of communication that you noticed.
- Experience the emotion associated with this character's moods.
- Knowing a character well can help you to enhance the messages that it brings to the audience.

## The Content and the Audience

The importance of knowing the content of the story and its various meanings has been stressed earlier in this chapter. Another useful aspect of knowing the story line from memory is that it allows the storyteller to tailor his/her delivery of the story line and its messages to the audience. The audience gives the storyteller feedback through its non-verbal response to the telling of the story. The keen observer can tell when it's time to pick up the tempo or to slow it down, to speak louder or softer, to gesture to the crowd or to focus attention on various members of the audience.

Some storytellers incorporate non-verbal responses of the audience into the action of the story. For example, "The crowd sat motionless as the king walked into the room," or "The audience felt fidgety as the emperor entered the palace," or "Jason sat staring with his hand under his chin," or "Just then, he rubbed his eyes and wondered about many things. This makes the story fit the actual reality of all or part of the audience. Pacing the audience in this way allows for a deeper rapport between the storyteller and listeners.

When the audience appears to be losing interest in the story, a change is necessary to get their attention. This can be accomplished in many ways, most of which are visual, auditory, or tactile cues. A visual cue might be the use of a picture, a hand gesture, a prop, or a puppet. An auditory cue can include raising, lowering or softening the voice, a snap of the fingers, a clap of the hands, the sound of music, or an increase in the speed of the voice. Tactile cues can include a touch on the shoulder, the raising of one hand, the acting out of the story, or the joining of hands.

The storyteller may be using the story to relax or to quiet the group and so, by using the word "quiet" or "relax" or "soften" several times in the story and, by changing the voice tone when pronouncing or saying the word, the message becomes embedded in the experience. Similarly, when the storyteller wishes to convey a specific message, or moral, e.g., treat others as you wish to be treated, the voice tone or pitch can be changed for that specific line or the storyteller can signal the audience with a wave of the hand or can actually touch a member of the audience when speaking the message. This technique marks the message out of the context of the story and causes it to stand out. When using these techniques the storyteller can deliver the message when it appears that the audience is ready. The storyteller may want to repeat a message throughout the story line in order to make it more obvious.

## Writing a Story

The next logical step for the child and youth care professional who is striving to use storytelling as an effective means of communication, is to write stories that are tailored to the child's individual needs and life situation. Stories that are written specifically for the child address the child's particular problem in a personal way, and they present specific strategies or lessons in a manner that the child can best appreciate. The writer can pay particular attention to the child's age, level of developmental functioning, particular interests, specific style of learning, and individual life situation while constructing the story. These personalized stories allow the child and youth care professional to tailor metaphorical interventions to as many aspects of the child's life as possible. As a rule, the younger the child, the more overt the connection between the child's life and that of the story's character(s). Thus, a four-year-old enjoys stories that are told which parallel their life identically. The older the child, the more covert the connection should be. Stories told to teenagers, for example, are more effective when the moral or lesson is not communicated directly in the story and when characters only remotely parallel the teenagers' lives.

## ♦ Exercise 14:5

- Identify a problem that you are experiencing.
- Give this problem a metaphorical name, e.g., Pain in the Neck could be a name for a problem with an annoying coworker; Crop Failure could refer to an unsuccessful attempt at developing a friendship with someone.
- Brainstorm and list all possible solutions to the problem. Remember that brainstorming allows for all possible solutions. Whether they seem to make sense at the time or not, write them down.
- Select the most desirable solution(s).
- Using a well-known children's story as a guide, write a story that identifies your problem, that includes all important characters, and that resolves the problem in the way chosen.
- Read through the story and decide which dramatic effects would be suitable in order to present your story to a group of children.

Writers who are in tune with their audience can create stories that seem to present the next step in the developmental maturity of the listener's life. Milton Erickson, a writer of such powerful stories, spent long hours creating precise metaphorical language that created profound changes in his patients. Dr. Erickson, towards the latter part of his career, used story alone to treat severe psychologically and emotionally damaged clients successfully. His stories were irresistible to the patient because he was able to present them in such a way that their content was tailored to the client's life experience so precisely that the client saw clearly which step to take next on the road to restoring psychological and emotional health (Rosen, 1982).

## ♦ Exercise 14:6

- Select a problem area that can be discussed openly with an individual child or a group of children, e.g., divorce, stealing, fighting, etc.
- Discuss this problem with the group, and categorize their statements according to these four areas:

- What were the sensations/emotions?
- What was seen?
- What was heard?
- What was said?

♦ Typical questions to ask the children using stealing behavior as an example are:
  - What did you feel just before you stole the bracelet?
  - What did you feel afterwards?
  - What did you see when you entered the store?
  - Did you have any pictures in your head?
  - What were you saying to yourself before, after, and during the time you stole?
  - Were there any sounds or people talking when you stole the bracelet?
  - Did you say anything out loud before, after, or during the theft?
  - Were there any sensations that you felt?
  - How were you feeling inside?
  - Was there any part of your body that felt sore, tense or just different?

♦ These questions are geared to obtaining information that can be placed into each of the four categories. Three or five words or phrases in each category is sufficient information.

♦ Be sure to write down verbatim what the child has said and make note of any mispronunciation or of the particular way it was said so that when the story is told, the storyteller can replicate the child's language and manner of speaking as closely as possible.

♦ Ask the child or group of children to come up with possible solutions or outcomes to the problem using a brainstorming technique.

♦ Now all of the information has been gathered and it's time to write your story.

♦ Select a context or type of story, e.g., animal story, science fiction, fable, etc.

♦ Write the story using as many of the statements collected as possible.

♦ Include most desirable solutions or outcomes generated by the group or the child, and include them as part of the story.

- Read the story and write in the margins the possible dramatic and visual effects that can be used to enhance the story.
- Read the story out loud to the group.

**Three apples fell from heaven,**
**One for the storyteller,**
**One for the listener,**
**And one for the one who heard.**

**ANONYMOUS**

## Activities

The following are activities to enhance the child and youth care professional's information about each child in the group in order to allow him to create more meaningful stories. These also allow the children to take part in story writing and storytelling, and they give them some insight into how stories and metaphor affect their lives.

### ♦ ADD A LINE

This is an old game played at many campfires, classrooms, and homes.

Ask the group to form a circle. The leader begins by making up the first few lines of a story. They stop and ask the person next to them to continue. The story goes around the group until each one gets a chance to add a line or two. The story may go around the group several times before it is completed.

### ♦ PHOTOGRAPHS

Cut out interesting and provocative pictures from magazines and back each of them with bristol board or construction paper. These pictures can be a way to introduce discussion using a theme or subject. Ask the children to write or to tell the story that each photograph says to them.

### ♦ TAPE RECORDING

Tape recorders are excellent tools to use for storytelling. They can be used in many novel and creative ways allowing the child to tell their own unique story.

Assign someone to be the interviewer (if there is more than one tape recorder, there can be several interviewers). The interviewer can interview any person in the group on a designated topic, e.g., early years, primary grades, family history, war, music, the environment and so on. The topic should give them the freedom to talk about their experiences and about what they think as individuals.

## ♦ ACT A STORY, TALE, OR MYTH

This activity allows children to live out a story in dramatic form. Taking part in the myth or tale can make it more meaningful.

Choose a favourite tale or myth. Allow children to audition for any or as many parts as they wish. Do not limit characters to humans or animals; children can sometimes derive more meaning or direction from playing a plant or inanimate object. The audition requires that they act out a small section of the character's part in the story. The adult leader or the group chooses who is best for what part (each part can be played by more than one person). Once the auditioning is over, the story is acted out by the group.

## ♦ LIFE HISTORY IN A LINE

This exercise is a more concrete way of telling the life story. It can be drawn from birth to the present day, or from birth to death, stopping off wherever the child decides. The life history can be represented by a straight line or by a circle.

Children often need time to collect necessary information for this exercise from their family members; therefore, an introduction to this exercise a day or a week prior to conducting it is advisable. The children are asked to recall significant events in their lives, e.g., birth, first steps, first words, day care, primary school, vacations, camps, divorces, deaths, injuries, failures, etc., and to make a list of these events in chronological order. If dates are available, they can be included in the exercise. (Younger children can be encouraged to make a pictograph by drawing pictures on small cards that represent significant events.) Provide paper large enough to allow them to mark out their life line or their life circle.

## ♦ STORY FOR STORY

Children intuitively know what to do to solve their problems, and this game can help the child and youth care professional to communicate in story form, and receive clues in the child's story as to how to help a child solve a problem.

Begin by telling the child a story about a character who has a problem and who finds a way of solving it. When your story is complete, ask the child to tell you a story. If the child and youth care professional listens closely, there are often unresolved issues or problems for the characters in the child's story; or, there is a style of problem solving that the child values. When the child has finished, the child and youth care professional tells a story that provides a strategy of problem resolution that either matches the style in the child's story, or is a more effective strategy than the ones already tried. This storytelling can continue as long as the child wishes to participate. This is also a useful way to develop a repertoire of characters with the child.

## ♦ MAKE BELIEVE

This exercise allows children to play with a favourite nursery rhyme, story, or fairy tale, and is an early beginning for the use of metaphor.

Ask the children to write out in brief a favourite story, fairy tale, or nursery rhyme. Instruct them to exchange their names and the names of their friends or relatives for the names of the characters in the story. When completed, these stores are to be read aloud to the group.

### Bibliography for STORYTELLING

Barker, P. (1985). *Using metaphors in psychotherapy*. New York: Brunner & Mazel.

Bettelheim, B. (1977). *The uses of enchantment*. New York: Vintage Books.

Burns, M. (1983). *Stories in child care*. Sarnia, ON: Author.

Erickson, M., & Rossi, E. (1979). *Hypnotherapy: An exploratory casebook*. New York: Irvington Publishing.

Gorden, D. (1978). *Therapeutic metaphors*. Cupertino, CA: Meta Publications.

Rosen, S. (1982). *My voice will go with you*. New York and London: W.W. Norton.

CHAPTER FIFTEEN

# ART, DRAMA, MUSIC, AND MOVEMENT

When Leroy walked through the doorway, he stopped and waited until his eyes became accustomed to the dimly lit, smoke-filled room. As his vision cleared, he saw musicians huddled in the far corner of the room. A flood of sound and emotion waved through his body; he groped for a place to sit so that he could give witness to this strange experience. Leroy's senses were bombarded as the stage lights exploded into reds, blues, and yellows. The musicians, frenzied in an attempt to express all that they held within, filled the room with a sound so rich that its blend with the atmosphere created shock waves through Leroy. The theme of their music was unintelligible and as Leroy tried to collect himself, he searched for some meaning to tag onto this experience.

The music was communicating;the crowd was responding; but he was unable to make sense of it; nothing in his experience could relate to the strangeness of the moment. He stopped questioning, closed his eyes, and let go of conventionality; he decided to let the experience direct him, instead of him trying to direct it. He listened intently and focused his attention on the three forms in front of him. They began to speak to him, to move him emotionally through the force of their music, their movements, and their use of colour and light. Their pain and joy, his and every human's was celebrated.The longer he stayed and participated, the more he discovered ways of understanding life.

> **Far from being a luxury, time and money spent on the arts enhances learning and development by reducing the stress of hurrying and by giving children an aesthetic perspective to balance the work day one**
>
> **DAVID ELKIND**

Understanding, appreciating, and expressing the self in terms of the art experience requires a shift from the logical, analytical frame of reference to one that is more creative and unorthodox. Leroy made this shift by opening himself up to the musicians' experience, and by allowing his heart and psyche to influence his interpretation of that experience. Children are often able to make this shift quite easily, allowing them more integrated experiences and ways of being that allow logic to sit side by side with creativity. This integrated self has great potential because it leaves the child a wider frame of reference with which to experience the world. This integrated self is often called being centered. The use of art, drama, music, and movement in the programming of activities for children and youth provides children with opportunities to exercise and utilize this ability to integrate their experiences.

Art, the play of muses, is also the natural expression of the self; it is play that expresses and records the feelings of being human. The child and youth care professional who makes use of programming in the arts possesses a very powerful, pragmatic and self-healing tool with which to nurture and educate the children in care.

The focus of this chapter will be upon art as a means of self-expression, upon drama as a way of providing insight, upon music as a mood-setting device, and upon movement to music as a vehicle of expression. The pragmatic orchestration of these mediums, their integrated potentialities, and their effect on the self-image of the child are the gifts they bear. The usefulness of the techniques discussed will rely upon facilitators who are able to make their own shift to the integrated self and who are able to foster this ability in others, and upon an environment that allows children sufficient freedom and structure to express themselves.

## ♦ Exercise 15:1

- Collect some art materials that you have at your disposal. Find a comfortable spot where you will not have any disturbances.
- Relax yourself using a favorite relaxation technique.
- When you are relaxed, concentrate on a feeling: sorrow, fear, jealousy, or anger.

- Try to allow your thoughts to flow in whatever way is comfortable.
- Symbols such as human figures, colour, motion, shapes, and words will come into your mind and cause your physical self to feel this emotion.
- When you feel that emotion, pick up the art materials and create. Do not erase or plan your picture but allow the symbols to take shape on the paper.
- When you have completed your composition, stand back and view it as a stranger would.
- What does the picture say?
- Now give your work of art a title.
- What is this piece of art telling you about how you experience this emotion?
- Write down some of the more important aspects of this experience and discuss them with a friend.

## FACILITATOR

The child's need to create, to fantasize, to use intuition is a drive and a natural way of self-expression which is a major source of learning and personal discovery for the child. When a child is allowed to satisfy the drive to create in a way that best suits individual needs, self-esteem and self-concept will grow. The fewer restrictions on the child's ability to create forms a catalyst that increases the rate of personal growth. The most destructive restriction placed on children's art today is that of standards. It is said to be good or bad, age-appropriate or not age-appropriate, worthy of the bulletin board or not worthy, correct form or incorrect form, on topic or not on topic, and so on. These judgements, based on someone's idea of what is acceptable, have no place in the promotion of children's expression of self through the art media. They are useful in formal art instruction but not when art is being used as a vehicle of self-expression. In many cases, the adult's standards are unrealistic and counterproductive to creativity. They can be very inhibiting, especially in the early stages of experimentation and discovery for the child. If the goal were to produce competent artists, then perhaps criticism and value statements would be of some merit. The goal and philosophy behind creative expression of self through art mediums is to provide an atmosphere of acceptance and respect in which the child can be expressive and create something truly individual and, in this creation, find value and self-regard. This philosophy gives sufficient license to allow the child to explore and create in whatever way best suits his/her needs. It also allows the child to make use of areas of the brain that are seldom exercised. Intuition and resourcefulness are often not given the emphasis they warrant.

In his book, *Development Through Drama*, Brian Way states, "Intuition might well be considered the most important single factor in the development of inner resourcefulness and full enrichment depends on this inner resourcefulness" (Way, 1967, p. 5). Within this philosophy of free expression, the child relates to the child and youth care professional as an equal. The adult becomes the resource person, the facilitator, and part of the art experience. This role complements the activity and the goal behind the activity. Once again, the least intrusive role provides optimum opportunity for personal and interpersonal growth.

Limits and structure are also important in the provision of activities in the arts. They provide safety, predictability and order to the experience. Children need to feel safe in their environment in order to feel free to express themselves. Rules that limit invasion of personal space, ridicule, and destruction of materials are necessary in order to provide safety and order. Predictability that materials and boundaries will always be there also allows the child to feel safe and free. Order insures that materials will be in the same place, that space will be free of obstacles, that sequencing of activities when necessary will be implemented, and that there will be a way to begin and end each activity.

The child and youth care professional may choose to take an active role as facilitator in the child's experience. This role of facilitator has been discussed several times in the preceding chapters, and involves the basic skills of relationship building, pacing, and the awareness of when to intervene and when to disengage in learning situations. It also requires the adult to learn and to demonstrate techniques in the arts, not necessarily to the point of mastery, but of sufficient skill to provide examples of choice for the artist. The adult who takes an active role in the art experience through his/her own creations can provide leadership in experimentation, styles, and appropriate behavior. The role of resource person expects the child and youth care professional to be able to readily access materials and to provide avenues for the child to access information and style in order to enrich the art experience.

Children communicate through art and their expressions are statements about themselves. In most cases, these statements are obvious and need not be responded to directly at a conscious level. The child and youth care professional may wish to use a portion of the art experience to ask children to talk about or translate their creation into their own words and meanings. Unless the child care professional is trained in art therapy, these discussions should center around the child's interpretations and the child's response to the questions from the others. Often the child will wish to interpret a dance, drawing, or creation on his/her own and this should be encouraged. The art work should never be judged or analyzed by the adult group leader or other children in the group. A good technique is to provide time at the end of the art period, or throughout the period, for children to tell the story or theme behind their creations. Sometimes questions from the adult or child observer are appropriate for clarification or to make an observation provided that these are respectfully presented and that the artist feels comfortable with this form of dialogue. An open-ended, positively oriented discussion of what the art work communicates is a very effective way of using art as an enjoyable and therapeutic exercise. These observations and clarifications can be useful contributors to the growth and development of the child's self-esteem.

The free expression of art is often a metaphor for children's life situations; therefore, it can provide insight for them into who they are, and possibly why they and others behave in the way that they do. Child and youth care professionals can provide the child with an opportunity to become more aware of what is being expressed. This must be done with great sensitivity to the artist, and with the understanding that what adults see in children's art is sometimes influenced by their own unconsciousness. Interpretations need to take the form of questions to the artist and not as statements of fact. These questions are meant to stimulate the child to become more self-aware and not to interrogate or to force self-disclosure. Self-disclosure sometimes happens as children become aware of their emotions and experiences as they are depicted in their art. These moments need to be handled with sensitivity and respect for the child. Most interpretations and, thus, insights come best from the artist, and in these cases the child and youth care professional can only patiently wait until they are realized.

Once the primary barrier, the observer of the child's art, is sufficiently de-emphasized; the secondary barrier (to the spontaneous expression of the self), in some cases, is the child's own inhibitions. Resistance to trying something new, like resistance to change, is a perfectly healthy response demonstrated by most humans. Children need time to become comfortable with certain mediums and situations; therefore, time and patience have no equal. Art forms can be incorporated in other more familiar activities or in conjunction with one another to provide more varieties of response. Inactivity is a very productive state, and often a very necessary stage of development. It, too, should be encouraged and fostered. This assures children that a wide variety of responses are acceptable, and that they are free within the confines of their imaginations to do what is most important for them at that given moment. Once the child has realized this state, the possibilities for creative expression, introspection, and learning are innumerable.

## ♦ Exercise 15:2

- Take out paper and markers, crayons, etc. Find a quiet and comfortable spot. Quiet yourself until you feel fully relaxed.
- Think back through your childhood to your early years, five years old to ten years old.
- What pictures, symbols and colours come to mind?
- Allow as much time as you need, thinking about your early years and remembering.
- Draw the most important symbols, pictures, etc., down on the paper and add words if you like to better communicate their meaning.
- Step back and look at your picture as if you were a stranger.
- What do you see?
- Share your drawing with a friend and try to explain it.

## The Creative Milieu

Essential to the success of any expressive art project is the environment. The environment must allow for uninhibited expression. The facilitator must complement this feeling of freedom with an ability to provide direction and resources to the child in order to maximize the child's experience.

The ideal art environment would be one that allows the child to experiment in all the major art forms: art, music, movement, and drama. Two work areas are needed: one, an area large enough for each child to have space to work individually, and two, a space large enough for all children to move freely without fear of collision. Furniture can be rearranged in a classroom; tents and shelters can be erected on playgrounds and camping areas; or, a room with free access to a play area can be converted into excellent art environments.

Adequate lighting, heating, and a source of water are next on the list of essentials. Once the housing needs are met, an adequate source of materials and equipment will complete the physical needs of the environment.

The arrangement of equipment and materials depends upon the types of programs provided for, and upon the physical layout of the room. Equipment and materials should be arranged to provide for easy transition from one idea or activity to another. For example, clay, finger paint, painting, and related activities should be situated close to a water supply for easy access and clean up. The sound system should be easily transferred from one area to the next and be equipped with headphones to allow for quiet listening. The more portable the materials and the equipment, the more adaptable and fluid the environment. Simplicity in wall design and room furniture should provide a sense of order and openness for creative thought and maximum use of space. Decor should reflect a balance in terms of providing a variety of experiences for the artist without overstimulating and confusing the child.

## List of Materials

### Art Materials

Materials can include sand, mud, clay, plasticine, play dough, finger paint, oil paint, acrylic paint, poster paint, water colours, pastels, chalk, charcoal, crayons, markers, pencil crayons, felt pens, pen and ink, pencil, glue, paper of various sizes, colours and textures, knives, sticks, rolling pins, and brushes; other natural substances to glue or attach to paper or alone to create with, such as bark, small stones, or dried flowers. Easels, boards, tables, chairs or cushions, drop sheets for clay, finger paint, and paint shirts for all can also be provided.

### Drama Supplies

Some examples are costumes, old clothes, hats, shoes, glasses, canes, make-up, jewelry, body paint, puppets, marionettes, and a puppet stage. Various props for improvisation can be hoops, sticks, rope, scarfs, sheets, blankets, etc.

### Music Accessories

You can use various percussion instruments like blocks of wood, metal bars, triangles, drums, maracas, tambourines, bells, etc. Other instruments can include the ukulele, harmonica, guitar, piano, banjo, trumpet, recorder, etc. A sound system, various tapes, and discs can be utilized.

## ♦ Exercise 15:3

- Find a comfortable spot and relax your physical self and your intellectual self.
- Summon up your creative abilities and imagine the perfect room for expression of the arts.
- Take all the time you need to create this ideal space in your mind.
- Write down a rough list of its features.
- Draw the floor plan of this room, complete with details.

## Art: As a Medium of Self-Expression

The manipulation of art materials to express feelings, thoughts, and behaviors is a powerful form of communication and, in some instances, the most effective way for a child or youth to discuss and gain understanding and insight into how s/he relates to the world. Regardless of the sophistication of the art work, be it a scribble drawing or a detailed mural, the artist expresses a part of the whole of his/her self-image. The expression of feelings and thoughts through the use of art can result in a purging of these feelings, as a release from them or as an expression of them in order to gain insight and understanding. These possibilities provide therapeutic outcomes for the artist. Children's natural closeness to their emotions and the fact that they are not always able to understand or effectively deal with them, makes art programming very beneficial. The style of expression and type of communication depends upon the child and the art medium selected.

The most fundamental art medium is a pointed stick and the earth. Children write their names in the sand; they draw plans of action and boundaries for games in the earth; and they create three-dimensional objects out of the earth itself. Finger paint, plasticine, clay, and sand sculptures are more primitive, earthy, and base mediums. These basic art agents often provide a vehicle for the expression of basic urges and desires as well as provide a means of regressing to an earlier and more primal time of life. Art tools vary from lead pencils to felt pens, from poster paints to oil paints, and from small pieces of white paper to large rolls of newsprint for making murals. The mediums used and the size of paper or physical boundaries of the art work vary considerably. Children can be given the opportunity and encouragement to explore as many mediums of expression as are possible within the limitations of the environment. Play dough, clay, papier mâché, wood, metal, and so on provide a third dimension in the art experience. Pounding, pinching, squeezing clay, hammering nails, and splattering paint can also be a way of releasing tension and anxiety. Drawing and colouring an abstract or a scene can offer the child a novel way to communicate. Craft mediums such as bark, paper tubes, magazine photographs, feathers, and string are useful in collages and three-dimensional art projects. The most effective art program provides a wide range of mediums and the opportunity to use them spontaneously. This variety and spontaneity allows for a myriad of opportunities for self-expression.

## ♦ Exercise 15:4

- Take out some art materials, whatever you have available.
- Find a peaceful spot in your environment and slow your thoughts down.
- Relax your body and mind, erasing the stress.
- Go back in time and remember your family.
- Picture in your mind each character.
- Listen to their voices.
- Touch them in your imagination.
- When you have systematically thought of each character, take up your art materials.
- Draw each character and arrange them into a family portrait or the family involved in an activity.
- When your picture is complete, reflect on it and your experience.

## Drama: As a Way of Providing Insight

Drama allows children to express their feelings and to experience the feelings of others; it provides insight into their view of the world and how others view it.

Drama can provide insight for the child in two ways; one, in the role as performer, and two, in the role of observer of the action. The child as performer can gain insight by experiencing, through acting, how different characters view the world and how they relate to it. Children can also gain personal insight by playing themselves or by playing a character most like them. Further insight can be obtained through discussing the thoughts and emotions that arise in the course of the acting. Children, in their role as observers, can observe how different characters think, behave, and relate. They can choose to use these characters as models of desirable and undesirable behavior, of effective and ineffective ways of thinking, and of acceptable and unacceptable ways of relating to others. When observing their own behavior as it relates to a character in a play or as someone playing them in a short skit, children get a chance to remove themselves emotionally from the situation and to view their behavior. This objective experience often allows them to gain a lasting insight into how their behavior affects others and in turn, themselves.

Life skills can be taught through role-playing social situations such as travelling on the bus, how to phone home, asking friends to dance, handling issues with parents, or speaking in public. Preschoolers take on various roles in their play in order to learn and to practice social skills. The dramatic play area and housekeeping area are very busy and well-used spaces in the day care center. Middle childhood individuals enjoy skits, mime, and short plays that have simple plots and little dialogue to remember. Preadolescents and adolescents enjoy a variety of styles of drama such as humorous skits, air guitar, rock musicals, improvisation and, for some, epic dramas, classical plays, and Broadway shows. The activity section of this chapter has various warm-up exercises and dramatic activities that will assist in the use of drama with children. Chapter Thirteen (Relaxation, Imagery, and Guided Fantasy) has exercises that are excellent ways to set the stage for the child to utilize drama as a teaching, learning, and self-fulfilling activity.

Drama is also movement and non-verbal communication. The movement activities in this chapter will assist children to learn how to manipulate their bodies in order to better express themselves. Mime and improvisation are excellent ways to increase the child's dramatic skills and talents. Drama is a form of the arts that allows children to strengthen not only their ability to communicate, but also their ability to understand better the communication of others. Life is a drama and, for many children, this drama is a struggle. The child and youth care professional, through the use of drama, can offer insight and new strategies to assist children in coping with life's struggles and can provide opportunities for them to realize their abilities and strengths.

## ♦ Exercise 15:5

- Find a comfortable spot and relax.
- Concentrate on a relationship problem you are experiencing currently or have had in the past and that is unresolved.
- List the key persons involved.

- List any other characters that are partially or indirectly involved.
- Invent, or use, a real scenario with all the characters involved, e.g., family picnic, a day shopping, a sport event, etc.
- Select the indirect characters and take on their personae in your scenario.
- Think the scene through, taking on each role.
- Now choose the key characters and play their roles out.
- Finally, play yourself and be aware of key emotions, thoughts, and behaviors.
- When all the characters are played, slow down your breathing and relax.
- Clear your mind, slow your pulse rate and allow your thoughts to take you to a favourite peaceful place where your information will be assimilated.
- Relax for five minutes.
- Write down your new awareness of the characters and their roles.

## Music: As a Mood-Setting Device

Music is a powerful medium. It is a strong emotional communication and it has the ability to change the emotional experiences of its listeners. It can set a mood. There is such a wide variety of music available that to list it all here would be impractical; therefore, the following suggestions will only scratch the surface of possibilities. Music has a number of uses: it can be used to relax the child and as background for a relaxation exercise; it can be used in conjunction with the art experience as inspiration or as background; it can be used in drama exercises and productions in a variety of ways; it can be used as impetus in movement exercises to allow the child to express themselves and to interpret the music through their body; it can be used as dance music; and it can be used for entertainment and listening pleasure. Classical music by the various composers provides a wide range of uses for the programmer: Mozart, Beethoven, Chopin, Korsakoff, Strauss, Bach, Vivaldi, Wagner, Pachelbel, Handel, Mendelsohn and Satie are excellent sources. New age music by composers such as Ray Lynch, Michael Jones, Andreas Vollenweider, and many others provides good background and expressive music. Children's music by Sharon, Lois and Bram, Raffi, Bob Schneider, Pete Seeger, Peter, Paul and Mary, Sesame Street, Hap Palmer, and others are excellent sources for games, listening pleasure, dance, and background music. Popular, folk, and country music are also useful sources for all types of situations. The wider the variety of exposure to music, the more varied the experiences for the children and youth. There is no real shortcut to finding the right piece of music for the specific situation; a good strategy is for the child care professional to listen to the particular piece of music selected, then to experiment with the group, and to ask for feedback. Sometimes children will want to bring in their own favourite pieces or they can make suggestions for the group leader. When music is utilized, it has a way of adding a special element to the group experience that can add cohesion and a sense of belonging; to the individual, it can add a sense of personal autonomy and positive self-esteem.

## ♦ Exercise 15:6

- Research and locate tapes, discs, and records that are available to you. Try to select a wide range of musical types and styles. Listen to these selections as an educator and care giver and select music that will be most useful to your group of children listing them in the following categories:
- RELAXATION: soft, quiet music that will slow down the activity level, reduce the amount of verbalization, and relax or deeply relax a group of children or youth.
- EMOTIONAL EXPRESSION: all types of music that will inspire anger, fear, joy, pride, sorrow, courage, and so on.
- INSPIRATIONAL: all types of music that will inspire self-expression, either through dance, movement, and/or art.
- NARRATIVE: some musical compositions tell a story.
- PLAY: music for games also comes from all types of compositions and is music that enhances enjoyment of the activity.
- Record the title of the composition, its author or performer and where this piece of music is available.
- Now you have a beginning of a list of music that you will find useful for your work with children and youth. As you use music with children ask them for feedback and suggestions so that your list can be most effective. Update and revise your list every six months.

## Movement: As a Vehicle of Expression

Movement is the expression of being alive; it is natural, necessary and, in many ways, life giving. Movement, as a means of self-expression and communication, can be a positive and healthy vehicle for children to understand and feel comfortable with their emotions. Movement expresses time, space, weight, force, locomotion, cooperation, isolation, and mood. When children are provided with opportunities to express themselves, non-verbal communication is often the most valid. Movement in the programming of activities for children and youth provides a vehicle in which the child can express what they cannot put into words. The diversity with which the physical self can clearly express the unconscious self makes movement activities excellent additions in all programming. There is self-expression in the way a toddler moves across the nursery floor, in the way a preschooler climbs, in the games of tag with school-age children, in the way an adolescent walks and, in all this common movement, certain individuality exists. Activities such as art, drama, yoga, gymnastics, sports, dance, music, and play itself are a coordination of movements that express who I am and how I feel about myself.

Creative movement is unstructured movement and it is the way a child moves in time and space. It can be expressed using music as an inspiration, or the child can create his/her own stimulation. The activity can purge emotions from the past; it can create emotions in the present; it can foster fantasies about how it will be in the future. The non-verbal expression of the self allows the child to reveal feelings without the fear of reprimand, questioning from others, consequences, justification, explanation, embarrassment and, at times, conscious awareness. Creative movement is an excellent activity for children who are non-verbal, who are resistant to talking about their feelings, who have experienced trauma, and who are unaware of their feelings. The other aspect of creative movement is its effect on the physical development of the child. The unstructured quality of creative movement eliminates failure and thus, frees the child to move in whatever way is desired. The movement to music provides the child with an opportunity to practice motion skills with a beat that will enhance coordination. Body awareness is also an aspect of creative movement that can be utilized in programming. Specific parts of the body can be emphasized and used in creative movement to enhance their awareness and coordination. Creative movement, like centering, can assist in the integration of mind and body. The child who expresses emotion and thoughts non-verbally integrates the physical self with the intellectual and emotional parts of the self.

Creative movement activities can be done seated, lying, standing, and moving the whole body or specific parts. The amount of space necessary depends upon the activity and the number of participants. The milieu should conform to the conditions pointed out in the section on creative environments in this chapter. Also, the selection of music and props can be useful as it allows for the integration with the other performing arts outlined in this chapter.

## ♦ Exercise 15:7

- This exercise goes very well with relaxing music.
- Begin this exercise by standing up and walking slowly around the environment that you are now in.
- As you move slowly, relax yourself to allow your attention to center on your physical self.
- Let your whole concentration focus on your body and how it moves in space.
- If space is at a minimum, you might want to visualize yourself walking in a slow, relaxed manner.
- As you put your attention to the physical experience of movement, be aware of tight muscles, joints or rigidity in the skeleton.
- Also concentrate on all strong sensations and on which area of the body they originate from.
- Begin to experience in a new way how your physical self occupies space and how it moves through space.
- Make a mental note of all images, memories, sounds, and emotions that you experience as you do this exercise.
- When you have moved for approximately ten to fifteen minutes, sit down with a friend and talk about your experience or write about your experience.

**If you paint, close your eyes and sing.**

**PABLO PICASSO**

## Activities

### ♦ SCRIBBLE DRAWING

Sometimes it is difficult to get started, and children need a structure to help them begin to create. The scribble drawing provides such structure.

Instruct the children to choose a colour of the art medium provided and a sheet of paper. They should, then, find a spot in the room where they feel comfortable and alone with their thoughts. (This exercise can also be done to music.) Once they feel comfortable, they are to take the colour and scribble over the sheet of paper. Allow them to scribble for approximately one minute. When they have finished, they are to look at their page from all different angles in order to locate familiar shapes, figures, or objects that are within the scribbling. Similar to the way we see shapes in the clouds on a cloudy day, the children are asked to discover these shapes on their paper. The group is then instructed to outline one of these shapes in a different colour. They will get this different colour by trading with a group member. When the outline is completed, they are to give their drawing a title.

### ♦ THE BLOB

This is another technique useful when the artist is stuck or does not know where to start.

When the art materials are passed out, the children are instructed to dab or drag the paint brush onto the paper. Next, they are to create a drawing using the dab or drag.

### ♦ CRAYON TAG

This is a good ice breaker or rapport-building exercise.

Using a large sheet of paper for each pair of children and one crayon each, instruct them to draw a racetrack onto the sheet of paper. When their track is complete, they are to take turns chasing each other's crayon along the track. One player will go first and start drawing his crayon down the track; the other player is to chase him and try to reach the end of the track first.

A game of tag can develop when one player chases the other player's crayon using the paper as the playing area. When the chaser tags the opponent's crayon, then they switch roles.

## ♦ PARTS DRAWING

This is a good group activity and requires team cooperation.

Divide the group up into small groups of four or five. Distribute art materials and instruct the group to draw a composite drawing of a person. Each member draws a different part of the anatomy. When the drawing is completed, they are to give their person a name.

## ♦ MASKS

Masks are very self-revealing and make an excellent activity in which to explore self-esteem.

Distribute pie plates, crayons or paints, construction paper, and assorted materials, e.g., bark, feathers, shells, beads, etc. Instruct the children to use the material provided and create a mask.

Masks can be made from papier mâché using a frame of chicken wire as a mold. They can be made from rolls of plaster used in the making of casts. These rolls can be obtained through a medical supplier. For this mask, the group is paired up and the masks are made, using the human face as the mold. The pair is instructed to choose who will go first. This person is to cover their face with vaseline. The plaster rolls are moistened and laid across the face to form a mask. The person can choose to have holes made for the eyes, nose, or mouth. They must have at least the nostrils or the mouth clear in order to breathe. The mask will dry in approximately fifteen minutes. As it dries, it will begin to pull from the face and when it is dry it will easily pull off the face. These masks can dry for a day and then be painted.

## ♦ SELF-HATE DRAWING

Children who have experienced self-hatred, self- doubt, and self-blame often get stuck in this spot and are unable to feel positively about themselves. This exercise offers the child a vehicle (art) in which to express this anger and then, in turn, express self-appreciation. Have art materials ready. Relax the group with a relaxation exercise.

- ♦ Now that you're feeling relaxed, I want you to concentrate on the times you get angry at yourself.
- ♦ You might get angry because of what you said or did or because you wished you had said or done something differently.
- ♦ Remember as many situations as you can.
- ♦ Become aware of how this feeling of self-hatred makes you feel.

- Where do you feel it in your body?
- What do you see? . . . Hear? . . . Feel?
- Think of how a picture of all this anger and hatred would look.
- What shapes are in your picture? . . . What colours? . . . What sounds? . . . What words?
- Now slowly erase that picture, remembering exactly how it looked.
- Now draw that picture on the paper provided.
- Relax the group a second time using a similar relaxation technique.
- Ask them to get an image or feeling of their positive self.
- Instruct them to remember the situations when they felt good about themselves and proceed in much the same way as in the first procedure.
- When they have completed the fantasy, the group is to draw this picture on the other side of the paper provided.
- Discuss with the group first, their drawing of self-hatred
- and then, their drawing of self-love.
- Ask them how do these parts integrate to become the person that you are?

## ♦ MIME

Mime is the oldest and most universal art form; it is both drama and expressive movement. There are endless possibilities for mime, and I have included a few ideas. All of these can be accompanied by suitable music.

### ♦ Popcorn

Instruct the group to find a space in the environment where they have room to move. Ask them to squat down and make themselves a kernel of popcorn. Suggest to them that the heat has been turned on and that they are getting warm, which is making them expand until, suddenly, they pop. Now try the same exercise with the whole group close together, as if in a popcorn popper.

### ♦ Flower

Instruct the group to find a comfortable space. Ask them to squat down and make themselves as small as possible. Suggest to them that they are a seed of their favourite flower. Tell them that it is beginning to rain gently, which is causing them to germinate and to grow into a beautiful flower. Caution them to grow slowly.

## ♦ Pass the Object

Ask the group to form a circle. Suggest that you have an imaginary object in your hand. Begin with hand miming a balloon and progress to a ball, medicine ball, worm, snake, flaming torch, etc. Pass the imaginary object around the circle.

A variation of this exercise asks the group to shape different objects out of imaginary clay. The first person hand mimes an imaginary ball, then claps his/her hands together as if to flatten it, then passes the flattened ball to the player on the left; the second player begins then to hand mime the formation of another object that once completed will be handed to the next person in the circle who will handle it as though s/he knows what it is. This same player then flattens the object and passes it on to the player on the left who in turn shapes a new object. This continues until the imaginary clay has been passed around the circle.

## ♦ Pick an Action

Write out a series of actions, e.g., starting an automobile, moving a piano, carrying out the garbage, skiing down a hill, eating dinner, painting a house, etc. Put each action on a slip of paper and into a bowl. Instruct each member to come up one at a time and pick an action. They have 30 seconds to act it out for the group. The group is to guess what the action is.

## ♦ Team Charades

Divide the group into two teams (you will need two separate rooms for this activity). Instruct teams A and B to go to their different rooms and to decide what action they will mime, e.g., fixing a flat tire, building a house, erecting a tent, building a campfire, etc. Team A then decides who will act out the mime. Team A calls in one member from Team B who watches the mime. When it is finished, the member from Team B calls in one of his/her teammates and acts out the mime for that person, who, in turn, calls in another member from the team and acts out the mime for him/her. This continues until the last member of Team B comes into the room and this person tries to guess what the mime that Team A presented represents. Usually, by the time this member tries to guess the mime, it is quite different from the original. If this person is unable to guess Team A's mime, *any* player from Team B can try to successfully guess it.

## ♦ MOVEMENT

These exercises can be combined with the mime exercises.

Select appropriate musical selections and ask children to move to the music as if they were:

1. An eagle or other bird soaring among the clouds
2. A seed growing into a beautiful flower
3. A member of a marching band in a parade
4. A honey bee flying from flower to flower to gather nectar
5. Clowns performing at a circus or carnival
6. Mountain climbers going up a steep mountain
7. Tiptoeing across the room so as not to wake your pet mouse
8. Ask the children to close their eyes and to imagine what the music is saying to them

**Props:** Scarfs, brightly colored strips of cloth or ribbons, balloons or small pieces of cord that can be used to enhance arm movement.

## ♦ ROLE PLAY

Role play can be an excellent way for children and youth to gain insights into their own behavior and into that of others.

Act out one or all of the following scenarios:

1. A teacher trying to control a room of unruly students
2. A child and youth care worker trying to motivate a group of bored teenagers
3. The classroom bully trying to get what s/he wants from a group of peers
4. A police officer among a group of gangsters trying to convince them to go straight
5. A group of teenagers trying to get a friend to try drugs, smoking or drinking
6. A room full of babies at lunch time in the daycare center
7. A pregnant woman stuck on an elevator who is about to give birth
8. A group of preschoolers asked to share their toys at nursery school
9. Any one of a number of situations that they group can suggest

**Variations:** Creatures from another planet, animals, robots, and machines can all be incorporated into some creative role playing by the group.

## ♦ AIR GUITAR

This is a favorite with teens and preteens. Select a favourite popular song that the group knows, usually one off the radio. Hand out props that can be used as microphones, guitars, horns, drums, etc. Ask the group to role play the song using the props. The results are often quite rewarding once the group gets over initial shyness.

## ♦ RECIPES

### ♦ Paint Mixture

This type of paint washes out of clothes and is an excellent medium for all ages. It can have a thick consistency, which is good for easel drawing. It can be mixed as thick as an oil paint or as thin as a water color.

In a saucepan, add one cup (1C) of dry laundry starch OR one and one half cups (1-1/2C) of liquid laundry starch. The dry laundry starch needs to be made into a paste by adding small amounts of water while stirring until it forms.

Add four cups (4C) to dry mixture OR three cups (3C) to liquid mixture and put on a low heat. Stir the mixture until it thickens.

Remove the mixture from the heat source and add one tablespoon (1Tbs) of glycerine or mineral oil. Mix well.

Add one cup (1C) of soap flakes or laundry detergent and mix thoroughly.

Store this mixture in the refrigerator or in an air-tight container.

This mixture is then mixed with dry tempera or poster paint, adding enough water to get the desired consistency.

### ♦ Finger Paint

In a saucepan, add five cups (5C) of water to one cup (1C) of cornstarch and heat on a low heat until the mixture thickens and is a clear color.

Allow the mixture to cool and then add one cup (1C) of soap flakes or laundry detergent and mix thoroughly. Powered tempera or poster paint can be added to get the various colors. Talcum powder can also be added to improve consistency.

## ♦ Play Dough

Mix two cups (2C) of flour and one cup (1C) of salt together in a mixing bowl. In a separate bowl, mix one cup (1C) of lukewarm water, one tablespoon (1Tbs) of salad oil, and two to four drops of food coloring.

Gradually add the liquid to the dry mixture of salt and flour and mix as you blend. Mix and knead well.

Repeat the procedure until you have all the different colors desired.

Store the play dough in a plastic bag or container and refrigerate or keep in a cool place.

## ♦ Flour and Water Paste

Mix one cup (1C) of flour with small amounts of cold water until a loose paste is formed.

Heat the mixture in a saucepan for five minutes (5 min.), stirring constantly.

Allow the mixture to cool and add a few drops of oil of wintergreen (optional).

Cover and refrigerate or store in a cool place.

## ♦ Papier Mâché

Buy premixed wallpaper paste or buy the powered paste and mix according to directions.

Cut or tear various sizes of strips of paper.

In a plastic tub or basin, soak the newspaper in the paste mixture.

There are various methods of using papier mâché. It can be layered over a frame usually made of wire, and especially for larger projects. It can be molded with the hands into various shapes when the paper is thoroughly soaked.

Experiment with this medium before presenting to the group. Papier mâché masks are a lot of fun.

## Bibliography for ART, DRAMA, MUSIC, AND MOVEMENT

Adamson, E. (1984). *Art is healing*. London: Conventure Ltd.

Elkind, D. (1987). *The hurried child*. Toronto: Addison-Wesley.

McMurray, M. (1988). *Illuminations: The healing image*. Berkeley, CA: Wingbow Press.

Nobelman, R. (1979). *Mime and masks*. Rowayton, CT: New Plays Books.

Rubin, J. (1984). *Child art therapy*. New York: Van Nostrand Reinhold Company.

Way, B. (1967). *Development through drama*. London: Conventure Ltd.

Wiesman, A. (1975). *Making things book 2*. Toronto: Little Brown & Co.

Yardley, A. (1988). *Senses and sensitivity*. London: Rubicon Publishing.

CHAPTER SIXTEEN

# SPECIAL PROGRAMS

Maurice, ex-gang leader of the Scorpions, who had lived a life of crime, was now making his last turn on to the final leg of a twenty-six mile foot race. In a way, he had trained for this race all his life and today he was fulfilling a life-long dream. He smiled as a wheelchair competitor raced past him and in a faint whisper said, "You can make it."

"Man, can those guys fly!" he thought. "Handicaps are in the eyes of the beholder." Upon thinking this, he was reminded of the handicaps he had to deal with in his lifetime. The poverty, the drugs, the violence and, worst of all, the desperate awareness that no one cared. "I have overcome all that," he said to himself. "Thanks to God and my friends and now another milestone in my recovery." The last mile of the race was now before him and Maurice knew that this was a very critical part of his conquest. It is at this point that many runners lose their concentration, injure themselves or drop from exhaustion. He stayed focused by reciting his affirmations, "I am lovable and capable. Nothing is out of my grasp."

As he chanted, his thoughts drifted to the one person who had been the most influential in his personal growth. Jack, a youth worker, had met him on the street one day and struck up a conversation with him. This encounter changed his entire life. It was a slow and painful journey with many hard times. Five years ago he had been on the streets in New York and, now, he was about to complete the Boston Marathon. He smiled as the finish line came into view and thanked himself for giving what only he could give. A gift of the self.

**The importance of being put in touch with the pain and pleasure in life, with your feelings and experience as they really are, is that it frees you to make the most realistic and positive adjustment to the world.**

**DAVID VISCOTT**

Special programs are for special people and so they must be conducted by special people. The experienced child and youth care professional with the proper support of co-workers, hospital or agency staff is such a person. Special programs helped a special person like Maurice to fulfill a life-long dream. They were instrumental in changing a troubled young man into a healthy disciplined young adult.

Special programs are not intended for the rookie child and youth care professional or student of child and youth care unless co-facilitated by a seasoned professional. They require in-depth planning and on-going supervision. A support staff of psychiatrists, psychologists, social workers, or other experienced personnel is necessary to the safety and effectiveness of the programs.

The following program guides are intended to act as parameters for your individual program needs. They cover the basic issues in each program area and provide a variety of ways in which to stimulate discussions. The child and youth care professional may add, subtract, and rearrange the program structure to suit a specific group's needs. Stories that pertain to the topic are an excellent way to begin and end the program. Games and activities that allow children to express themselves in all areas of development round out the effectiveness and the overall enjoyment of the program.

# Topic One: Emotions, Thoughts, and Behaviors

This group format is an excellent way to begin any special programming. It orients the children to understand their emotions and the connections that feelings, thoughts and behaviors have with one another.

## Session I: Positive and Negative Thoughts

Explain to the group what a positive thought is. For younger children you may have to help them with the concept, through examples and/or props. Ask the group to think of one or two thoughts that make them feel good.

Conduct a session around the examples from the group members so that they understand what a positive thought is and what effect that thought has on them.

Positive thoughts make us feel positive and usually motivate us to act in a positive way.

Now explain to the group what a negative thought is. Ask the group members to recall one or two thoughts that make them feel uncomfortable or upset. Conduct a discussion around the examples given by the group. Negative thoughts cause us to feel negative emotions which often result in negative or hazardous behavior.

## Session II: Pleasant and Unpleasant Emotions

Ask the group to select two pleasant emotions and two unpleasant emotions or you may select the emotions that you feel your group needs to discuss, e.g., love or pride or anger and sorrow. Instruct group members to focus their attention on one of these unpleasant emotions and ask them to recall a situation when they felt this way. Organize a discussion around the examples given by group participants. When each group member has given an example, ask the group members to recall a pleasant emotion and a situation when they felt this emotion. Continue your discussion focusing on the specific pleasant emotion. When the group has completed this part, introduce another unpleasant emotion and repeat the process. Finally finish the discussion by asking group members to focus on a pleasant emotion and to recall a situation when they felt this emotion.

Complete this program with five to fifteen minutes of quiet play so that the group leader can mingle with group members in order to insure that no child is left with uncomfortable feelings.

## Session III: Acceptable and Unacceptable Behavior

Explain to the group what acceptable and unacceptable behaviour is. Ask the group to recall either a situation when they felt that their behavior was unacceptable or a situation where an adult or peer judged their behavior as being unacceptable. When each group member has an example of an unacceptable behavior, begin the discussion about unacceptable behavior using the group's examples. Ask group members to identify their emotions and thoughts prior to their unacceptable behaviors.

Now ask the group members to recall either a time when they considered their behavior to be acceptable or a time when an adult or a peer judged their behavior as being acceptable. When each group member has an example, continue the discussion on behavior using the group's examples. Ask group members to identify their emotions and thoughts prior to their acceptable behaviors.

## Session IV: The ABC's of Behavior

Draw a chart on the blackboard with four columns, column A, B, C, and D. Column A represents a situation; e.g., I was home watching television with my brother. Column B represents the thoughts that the group member was thinking during the situation; e.g., "This program is stupid." "I wish I could change it." "It is my television and I can change it if I want." Column C represents the emotions that the group member was feeling; e.g., bored, frustrated, or superior. Column D represents the behavior; e.g., I went over and changed the station and my brother, Todd, got angry. Ask the group to think of a situation when they got into trouble for their behavior. Once each group member has an example, ask each member of the group to briefly explain their situation. As each member gives his example, determine if the example is suitable for the exercise. If the example is unsuitable, ask them to think of another example, perhaps giving them a better idea of the type of situation that you would find acceptable.

Now ask the group to find a comfortable position. Play some music that will set the mood for relaxation and conduct a relaxation exercise. When the group appears to be relaxing, ask them to focus their attention back to the situation they used as an example. Ask them to become aware of how they were feeling both physically and emotionally before, during, and after their situation. Ask them to recall some of their thoughts before, during, and after the situation. Ask them to observe and to listen carefully as they recall this situation from the past. Give them all the time that they need to complete this process. When each member of the group has returned from their relaxed state, refer the group to the chart with columns, A, B, C, and D.

Ask group members to share their examples and then to fill in each example into the columns on the chart. As each member recounts his/her situation, point out how thoughts and emotions affect the behavioral outcome. Suggest to the group that sometimes people blame others for their feelings and behaviors but they are often a result of how the individual thinks about the situation. Often when individuals change their thoughts or emotions their behavior changes as a result. Explain also how behavior can affect emotions and thoughts. Sometimes it is difficult to change how we feel about certain situations; however, if we change our thinking and/or our behavior, our emotions change on their own.

## Session V: Linking Feelings, Thoughts, and Behaviors

This session can be a continuation of session IV or it can be done separately.

Ask group members to recall a situation where their behavior was considered inappropriate. Relax the group members and ask them to recall the situation and to be aware of how the situation looked, sounded, and felt. Suggest that they can recall all the visual material from that time, all the auditory information and all the emotions and sensations they felt. Give the group sufficient time to complete this process.

When each group member has returned from a state of relaxation, pass out paper and coloured markers. Instruct the group members to draw the situation that they are working on, including all the detail that they remembered.

When the art work is completed, ask each group member to explain his/her picture. As group members share their situations, ask them about their emotions and thoughts during the episode. Help them to become aware of the link between emotions, thoughts, and behaviors.

## Session VI: Observing the Experience

This too can be a continuation of Sessions IV or V.

Instruct the group to find a comfortable spot and to begin to relax. Use relaxation techniques in order to relax the group. Ask them to recall a situation when they were punished or confronted as a result of their unacceptable behavior. Explain that they can use their memories to recall the situation in its entirety. Suggest that they will become aware of all that they saw, heard, and felt during this episode. Give them all the time they need to complete this process. When all the group members have returned from their state of relaxation, ask them to form a semi-circle.

Instruct each member to recount his/her situation to the group and have each choose other group members to portray the main characters. They must also choose someone to play themselves. When all the characters are represented, the group member, with the help of the group leader, will direct this vignette until each character has his/her part well understood.

Now ask the players to act out the situation allowing the group member to experience it as an observer.

When this skit is finished, ask the group member to recount any new awareness and ask him/her to point out the connections between his/her thoughts, emotions, and behaviors as well as the consequences of that person's behavior on the other characters.

# Topic Two: Self-Image

## Session I: Identity

Conduct a relaxation exercise or a quiet game with the group before the discussion if necessary in order to slow them down to facilitate better concentration.

Present to the group the concept of identity. Identity consists of the experience of the physical self, the thoughts you have about you and your potential, how you feel about your potential for change and growth, and your perceived ability to assert yourself in order to reach your potential as an individual. The experience of the physical self or how it is to be in your body can be further explored when the group ponders these questions about themselves. Do you love your body? Do you take good care of your body? Are you proud of how you look? The thoughts concerning individual potential can be further explored in the answers to thes questions: Am I a good person? Am I intelligent? Do I have a good future? Self-esteem is also part of the identity in that it represents how you feel about yourself and your potential for change and growth. Will I be able to make it? Do I have a good feeling about myself? Can I handle life's experiences? Will I always be stuck in the same old rut? Finally, your ability to assert yourself so that you can reach your potential as an individual can be explored through the answers to these questions: Am I self-determined? Can I motivate myself? Will I be the man or woman, girl or boy, I wish to be? After explaining and discussing the idea of identity, pass out paper and markers and ask the group to draw a full figure self-portrait. Explain to the group that this and all other art work will be kept until the program is completed and then they will have their art work returned. This first self-portrait can be a useful assessment tool when compared with the last self-portrait done at the completion of the program.

When the self-portraits are completed, ask the group to turn their pages over and to copy these four words: body, concept, esteem, and determination. Ask them to rate how proud they feel about their bodies on a scale of one to ten with ten being the highest score. When they have decided on a number ask them to write it down beside the word,body. When completed, ask them to rate from one to ten how intelligent they feel. This score can go beside the word, concept. Now ask the group to rate themselves on how adaptable they are to change and increased responsibility, etc. This score can go beside the word, esteem. Finally, ask the group to rate themselves on how determined and motivated they are to actualize their potential. Can they work hard to achieve their goals? This score can go beside the word, determination.

Once the group has completed the scoring, ask for volunteers to show the group their drawings and to share their ratings on the back. Allow the children to explain only that which they will discuss willingly in order to maintain high levels of trust.

## Session II: Wants and Needs

Begin a discussion with the group about the concept of needs and wants by reading aloud the following statement: "A need is a desire for someone or something essential to the individual's physical, mental, emotional, or spiritual health. Everything else is a want." Have the group members list their desires and formulate a list of needs and wants on a flip chart or blackboard so all can see.

Discuss this concept further by going over the statement to ensure that group members understand what needs are.

Pass out paper and pencils and ask the group to refer to the list of needs and write beside the need the name of the person who most often fulfills that need for them. When the lists are complete have them share their lists. Discuss with the group their findings. Typically, the younger the person the more reliance there is on others to meet various needs. Ask the group to comment on how they feel about depending upon others to meet their needs.

Ask the group to form a circle and instruct them to silently mouth the words "I want!" Have them join hands and mouth the words "I want!" as if they are shouting it. Now ask them to say it out loud and say it like they are whining. Instruct them to say it again only now like they are taking responsibility for their wants. Now ask them to shout it out, "I want!" Discuss with the group their thoughts and feelings about the exercise.

Explain to the group that people sometimes use a passive or indirect way of asking for what they want or need. Sometimes they expect people to anticipate or always know what they want or need, a sort of mind reading.

Show the group various pictures of individuals alone and with others. Ask them to write down what the characters' thoughts are in terms of wants and needs. When the pictures are completed, ask the group to pair up with someone on the other side of the circle. This pair is to compare their answers for similarities. Discuss with the larger group the ineffectiveness of mind reading.

## Session III: Need Fulfillment

In this session the group is asked to determine who is responsible for meeting their individual needs. Ask the group to recall the discussion they had in Session II with reference to the people in their lives that fulfill their needs. Ask the group members to think of a time when their needs were not being met or they were only partially met. Have group members share these situations with the group. Find out what the child or youth did about this unmet need. Through questions and discussion, assist the group members to realize that they have an active role in ensuring that their needs are being met and part of that role involves asking for and deciding on what their needs are.

Divide the group into smaller groups of four to six. Tell the group that the point of this exercise is learning to ask in order to get their wants and needs met. Model for the group several examples of how to ask appropriately for what they need. This includes being specific about the want and being prepared if the answer is no. If the answer is no, help the children to learn to formulate questions that will help them to attend to this want or need, e.g., "No" might mean "Not right now" or "I'm angry with you" or "I don't feel that you need that right now."

Instruct each group to think of something that they can ask each member for, something which that person has the capability of giving. They will need to be specific about what it is that they want and to ask the person directly. They may ask the person to do something for them, e.g., bring your stamp collection to group; they may want someone to change his/her behavior, e.g., stop calling me names or call for me after school; or they may want to do something for or with the other person, e.g., can I come over to watch you practise football? When each member has thought of something for each member of the group, the group members take turns asking each other for something. The group members are instructed to answer honestly and to be responsible for following through with it with the other person. They are encouraged to say no if they really do not wish to do it or if they are unable to do it. When a member says no to a request, the group members are instructed to negotiate with one another until they reach a mutually satisfying solution.

## Session IV: Responsibility

Discuss with the group the concept that we are responsible for what we think, how we feel, and what we do and say. Most individuals appreciate their responsibility for their behavior and for expressing how they feel; however, some members may need help with understanding their responsibility for their thoughts. Refer to the beginning of this chapter (Topic I: Emotions, Thoughts, and Behaviors) and review the concepts that will help the group to appreciate or to recall the connectedness of these three areas.

Challenge the group members to think of a time when they were not responsible for their emotions, thoughts, and behaviors. When you feel that the group has an understanding of the concept of responsibility, conduct the following exercise. Pass out paper and pencils or markers to the group members and have them write down all of the negative statements that they have said to themselves, e.g., You're never going to make that team. You can't do math. No one wants to be with me. Ask them to list as many statements as possible. When the group is finished, discuss the effects these thoughts have on the individuals and on their self-esteem.

Now ask the group to write the positive statements that they say to themselves on a second sheet of paper, e.g., I am really excited about trying out for the team. I like math even though I have to work at it. I am a good person and I need a friend. Ask them to list as many as possible and then to invent a few more to fill the page up. Discuss the effects that these thoughts have on the individuals and their self-esteem.

## Session V: Discounting

Many children with self-esteem problems discount themselves, their environment, and the people around them. This contributes to the perpetuation of their feelings of low self-worth to a large degree. When children are asked to cognitively challenge these negative thoughts and attitudes, their self-image becomes more positive and appreciative.

Explain to the group that we all negate or put down individuals, ourselves, and places or situations. The discounting of individuals and ourselves is a good place to start. Ask the group to remember the exercise from the last group session, on negative self-statements. Pass out the paper and markers and ask them to write down statements that are negative towards others.

Briefly discuss the effect that these have on the other person and on the person who makes the statement.

On a new sheet of paper, ask the group to write down the negative statements that they often use to discount a place or a situation. Discuss the effect that these statements have upon the speaker and on the listener(s).

Collect the papers and markers and ask the group to divide into small groups; ask them to think of one positive statement that they could make to each individual in the group. Reinforce that the person receiving the positive statement must accept the stroke and not discount it. When each person has had a turn ask each member to make one positive statement about the meeting place or group environment.

## Session VI: Integration of the Selves

A healthy identity is determined by the individual's ability to integrate mind and body in the performance of meeting various needs. When an individual has a solid identity then that person can enhance other people's lives. The child or youth's identity as outlined in Session One consists of several aspects of the individual. Awareness for the child or youth of these aspects helps to appreciate where s/he stands in terms of self-worth.

Hand out paper and markers and ask the children to make four columns on their pages. At the top of column one write the word physical; in column two, write the word emotional; in column three, write the word intellectual; and in column four write the word social. Give the group examples of what would be considered a strength in all four categories, e.g., strong legs; ability to express anger; to do well in geography; or to enjoy being on the bowling team. Encourage them to write as many as possible and when they have completed this task ask the group to share one or two examples in each category. When they have completed the discussion, ask them to reconsider the four categories, then ask them to write with a different coloured marker in the areas that they would like to improve on. Discuss with the group this new list and help them see how this list can formulate into a set of goals which could help them to improve their overall sense of self.

Finally, ask the children to draw a portrait of themselves that reflects how they feel about themselves today and ask them to think about themselves and all the different parts of their identity.

# Topic Three: Peer Relationships

## Session I: Relationships

Slow the group down with a quiet game followed by a relaxation exercise. Conduct a guided fantasy that regresses the child to ages four or five and ask them to recall their early social experiences and the faces of their friends back then. Slowly guide them through their years until the present. Suggest that they will be able to remember many of their friends and then once they seem finished, slowly bring them back to a state of alertness. Pass out paper and markers and ask the group to draw all of the people that they remembered during their guided fantasy.

When the group has completed the drawings ask them to form a circle and discuss their drawings and their experiences of remembering friendships of the past.

Instruct them to go back to their drawings and with a pen or pencil to write down beside each friend, the positive quality of this person that made him/her fun to be with or the quality that was most attractive. The younger child may need some assistance and examples can be shared with them by the group leader. When this task is complete, ask the group to share the words that they have written. Suggest to the group members that the words they have on their drawings is a list of the qualities they look for in a friend.

## Session II: Strategies to Make a Friend

Children who have difficulty socializing often lack solid strategies to contact other children in order to make friends. They often choose each other because they feel the more social skilled children will not accept them. They have often been raised in families that reflect their lack of social skills. Often their parents are socially isolated and do not have the appropriate skills themselves to teach their children. Children and youth can be taught social skills.

Ask the group to pair up; one player is designated as A and the other as B. A's and B's are to face one another. Explain that there is an acceptable way to communicate that will encourage positive interactions and an unacceptable way to communicate that discourages positive interactions. Give the group an example of a positive way to ask for some help and a negative way to ask for help. The activity starts with A asking B first in a negative way and then, in a positive way to do something for them. Now it is B's turn to ask A both in a negative and then in a positive way to do something for them. The pairs proceed with the following requests in a similar manner: (a) not to play in a specific area; (b) someone does not want to play today; (c) the other player is not playing fair. When the pairs have completed this task, discuss with the whole group how it felt to make a positive and negative request as well as to receive a positive and negative request.

Ask the group to sit in a circle and discuss with them what strategies they use to make a friend. Ask them to close their eyes and to relax themselves and then to imagine that they have moved to a new town where they do not know anyone. Instruct them to describe how they would go about meeting a new friend. Discuss their different strategies and ask for feedback from the other group members. One good strategy in making friends begins with observing someone who seems friendly or interesting. This period of observation allows the child or youth a chance to decide whether this person looks and feels like someone to befriend. The second step requires the person to verbally contact the other to start up a conversation in order to gather more data as to the type, likes, and dislikes of that person. The final step requires an extended period of interaction with this person in a variety of situations. The more positive the interaction, the more solid the friendship.

## Session III: How to Develop Relationships

Open and honest communication is a sure way to maintain healthy friendships. So often children and youth do not communicate their thoughts and feelings towards one another and this can lead to relationship problems. Discuss with the group the importance of open and honest communication among friends. Much of the miscommunication that affects friendships occurs when one of the partners feels mistreated or feels that the other person does not care. Instruct the group on the proper use of an "I" statement (Gordon, 1970). The "I" statement goes like this: "I feel *(emotion)* when you *(behavior)* because *(consequence of behavior)*." Give group members several examples of "I" statements and then pass out paper and markers and ask them to construct one of their own. When the group is finished, ask them to pair up and to deliver their "I" statements to each other in a role play situation. Emphasize with the group that in order for the "I" statement to be effective, their body language must be congruent with their verbal language. Children often forget to include the last part of the "I" statement, "consequences of behavior," and this should be drawn to their attention. Once the group seems to be able to construct simple "I" statements, ask them to recall a time in their past when they were upset with someone but could not find the right language to say so. The group will need some time for this piece and they may need to lie down or to sit back and to relax quietly until they can come up with an example. When all group members have an example, ask them to pick a different partner. The pairs are instructed to take turns delivering their "I" statements. The person giving the "I" statement must give the person receiving it the background information with regards to the context of the scenario. When the "I" statement is delivered, the person receiving the message can give the sender feedback on how s/he felt and what s/he was thinking during the role play. This exercise can be expanded to allow the group members to role play a situation that required more than two players. When children are encouraged to use "I" statements with one another, conflict and miscommunications have an avenue for resolution.

## Session IV: Conflict Resolution

The first and most important part of conflict resolution is dealing with the emotions of the people who are involved. Ask the group to recall their last session which emphasized "I" statements. Instruct the group to formulate an "I" message that has to do with one person. Now have the group pair up. Once the pair has shared the scenario with each other and they both feel that they have enough information to role play, they are asked to continue. When partner A has delivered the "I" statement, partner B is to respond in terms of his/her feelings. The pair must stay with their feelings until they feel that they have been fully expressed. When the partners have completed both role plays, they are instructed to come back to the larger group and to subsequently discuss their experiences with the group. Complete this section by underscoring the need to express emotions before trying to problem solve.

Essential to all conflict resolution and problem solving is having enough options in order to successfully solve the problem and to accommodate the parties involved. Generating solutions, therefore, is the critical part. Instruct the group members to think of a problem that affects more than one person in the group, e.g., three of us have a detention tonight and we also have to catch the bus to the soccer game or, the group has a trip coming up but they cannot decide where to go. When a problem or problems have been identified, write the name of the problem at the top of a large piece of paper or on a blackboard, etc. Instruct the group that they are allowed to suggest any solution they like even if they feel it is not possible. The rest of the group must not judge or criticize any solution suggested. All suggested solutions are written down so that all of the group members can see. When all possible solutions are written down, go over them one at a time and eliminate those that are not possible. Reduce the list in this fashion until the best possible solutions remain.

Now ask the group to prioritize the remaining solutions. The problem now has possible and practical solutions that can be tried one at a time until the problem is solved.

Divide the group into small groups of three to five members. Give each group a paper and a marker as well as a problem to solve. The group is given five minutes to generate solutions and to come up with three workable solutions to the problems. When the small groups have finished, bring the larger group back together. Instruct each group to name their problem and the three possible solutions. When each group has done this, discuss with the larger group their experiences in the problem-solving exercise.

## Session V: Rescuing

One of the most dysfunctional roles that affect interpersonal relationships is the role of the rescuer. Ask the group to recall the last time they rescued a friend from a problem and to write the situations on the board or on a large sheet of paper. Select one or two examples that reflect the type of rescuing where the rescuer takes over the responsibility of the other person, i.e., friend interferes in the relationship of two others, who are trying to settle an argument. Ask the person, whose example you would like to use, to select players for a role play. When the scene is explained to the role players, they are asked to act it out for the group. The role play members are then asked to give feedback as to how they felt. The group members who watched the role play are also asked to give feedback. Ask the group, including role players, if they can think of another course of action for the rescuer.

Explain the role of rescuer as a well-meaning person who feels that the other person is unable to solve his/her own problem and, in a sense, the rescuer acts superior to the other. The person being rescued may be acting helpless when s/he is probably capable of solving the problem. The rescuer prevents the other from standing up for him/herself and from learning to solve problems on his/her own. Discuss with the group, alternate roles or strategies for the rescuer to take on so that person can support a friend but not take on the problem.

Divide the group into triads and ask them to designate who will be A,B, & C. To begin, A will be the victim and B will be the villain and C will be the rescuer.

Give them the following scenario or one of your choice to act out.

A is being bullied or coaxed by B to do something that A does not want to do. C comes in to confront B and stops B from bullying. Once they have acted out the scene, ask C to change the approach to the problem and enlist a strategy that allows A to solve his/her own problem. A is instructed to think, say how s/he feels, and take care of his/herself and needs.

When the triad has role played an effective solution, B becomes the victim, C becomes the villain and A becomes the rescuer. Repeat the process until all three have experienced each role. When the role playing is completed, ask the group to form a large group and to discuss their experiences.

## Session VI: Assertiveness

Children and youth need to learn assertiveness rather than aggressiveness or passive-aggressiveness when dealing with others in order to develop and maintain happy and healthy relationships. In order to be assertive, children need the proper guidance and vocabulary as well as a solid sense of self.

Instruct the group to form a circle; ask them to think about all of the things they have to do in a day or ways they have to behave. While they are thinking, pass out paper and markers. Ask the group members to write down a list of shoulds, oughts, and musts. All of the things you feel you must do, all of the things you feel you should do and all of the things you ought to be doing. When the lists are complete, ask that they share them with the group. When this has been completed ask the group to read their list again and to say before each one, I choose rather than I must. When each member has read his/her list a second time, ask how they felt when reading it the first time and then when reading it the second time (Hendricks & Roberts, 1977).

When children realize and appreciate that they choose to do what they do and that they can say no and face the consequences of that decision, they are better equipped to take responsibility for their behaviors. Assertiveness in interpersonal relationships requires the individual to be aware of and to take responsibility for feelings, thoughts and behaviors.

Assertiveness comes from a position of strength and is not intended to overpower or control the other individual(s). It is a way of stating clearly and without guilt or blame how the individual is feeling and thinking.

Ask the group to pair up and to find a comfortable spot in the environment where they can talk. Write out the following scenarios and pass one out to each pair. Write the following on the blackboard: Think, Say How You Feel, Take Care of Yourself and Your Needs.

(a) Someone has stepped in front of you in a long line waiting for the movie theatre. You and your date have been in line for the past thirty minutes. You decide to assert yourself.

(b) You have your final exams coming up and you need to study. Your family continues to make noise even after you have asked them to be quiet. You decide you must assert yourself.

(c) Your teacher has accused you of not doing your homework. You did your homework but forgot it at home. She is threatening to take you to the principal. You decide to assert yourself.

(d) A friend of yours has told a secret you had confided. Now your brother has found out and is going to tell your parents. You decide to assert yourself.

(e) You feel your friend is cheating on her exams and you are afraid that she will get caught. You decide to assert yourself.

When the group has played out the role plays, ask them to discuss their experiences. The ones who had difficulty can be encouraged to role play their scenario for the group and then to ask for feedback. The activity can continue until all members have had a chance to act out two or more scenes.

## Topic Four: Separation and Divorce

### Session I: Who's Responsible

One of the most difficult problems for children from separated families to resolve is understanding and appreciating their roles and the roles of their parents and other family members in terms of the break up of the family. Children have great difficulty understanding adult behavior and more specifically, adult thinking. As a result, children and youth almost always carry a portion of the guilt and resentment around the separation. Often they are unable to separate themselves from the problem and feel responsible in some way for their parents' pain. The first step to recovering from the trauma of marital separation involves the recognization of responsibility.

Begin this session by discussing with the group whose responsibility is it when they have a fight with their best friend. Instruct the group to recall incidents in their lives where they had a disagreement with a close friend. They may have lost their friendship and their trust. Ask each member to discuss their experiences in order to help them to appreciate what happened and who was responsible for what happened. Ask the group member sharing his experience to decide who was responsible for what happened in the relationship. Usually, once all the information has been gathered, responsibility for most interpersonal relationships is about fifty-fifty, unless there are extreme circumstances such as violence or mental illness.

Discuss with the group the concept of responsibility and shared responsibility in a relationship. A formal discussion format on responsibility can be found in Topic Two, on self-image, which was previously discussed in this chapter.

Ask the group to recall a time when they were present during an argument or disagreement between their parents. Instruct them to recall a time that is comfortable for them to think about and a time that will help them to understand their responsibilities in terms of their parents' problems.

You will need markers, two different sizes of paper, scissors and tape for this experience. One piece of the paper needs to be about 1/4 of the size of the other one. Pass out the larger sheet first, one to each group member. Instruct the group to draw one of the situations they were thinking about. Tell them to draw their parents, not anyone else. When this drawing is completed, pass out the smaller sheet of paper and instruct the group members to draw a picture of themselves proportionate to the size of the characters on the larger sheet. Pass out scissors or cut out the self-portraits for the group. When the group has completed the task, ask them to tape the self-portrait onto the larger picture relative to where they were during the argument.

Ask the group to talk about this experience and to share their feelings regarding when it was occurring and how they feel now about it. When each member has had a turn, ask them to remove their self-portrait from the larger picture. Ask the question, "Would your parents still be arguing if you were not there to hear it?" Discuss their answers to this questions in an effort to help them appreciate their responsibility.

Some children will have difficulty if their parents were arguing over them or what they did. The child may have to recall a time when they were not arguing over them. Another strategy would be to help them appreciate that parents have other options available to settle their differences. Some children's intellectual development will not allow them to fully appreciate the fact that it is solely their parents' responsibility but most will be able to understand the concept at a basic level.

## Session II: Mothers

Introduce the topic of the session by defining mothers in their various roles, i.e., biological mother, mother(s) who care for you physically and emotionally, mother(s) who teach about life, etc. Ask the group to find a comfortable spot, to close their eyes and to relax. Play relaxing music and ask the group members to recall both positive and negative experiences with their mothers. Allow them ample time to recall several experiences and periodically restate the instructions. When the group appears to be finished, ask them to slowly wake themselves up and then to form a circle quietly. Pass out paper and markers and ask the group to draw a picture of themselves with their mothers doing something. When they have completed their drawings, ask each member to share their experience and their drawing with the group.

Write the word Mother at the top of the board or flip chart. Ask the group to brainstorm around all the things that they enjoy doing with their mothers. When the list is exhausted, ask the group to look over the list and to select one or two things that they have not done with their mothers for a long time. Suggest to the group that the next time they want to do something special with Mom, they can discuss with her the possibility of doing one of the activities on the list.

Pass out paper and markers and ask the group members to complete the following statements.

**MY MOM**

1. One thing I like about my mom is ____________ .
2. One thing I do not like about my mom is ____________ .
3. I wish my mom would ____________ .
4. It is a difficult job being a mother because ____________ .
5. One way that I am the same as my mom is ____________ .
6. When my mom gets angry she ____________ .
7. When my mom feels happy she ____________ .
8. One thing my mom does not know about is ____________ .
9. I saw my mom sad when ____________ .
10. My mom taught me to ____________ .
11. One way that I am different than my mom is ____________ .
12. One more thing about my mom is ____________ .

Share and discuss the completed statements. Complete the session with the group members, recalling all of the lessons and strengths that each mother has passed on to her child.

## Session III: Fathers

Introduce the topic of this session by defining fathers in their various roles, i.e., biological father, father(s) who they interact with, father(s) who care for them and protect them, etc. Instruct the group to find a comfortable spot and to close their eyes in order to relax. Play some relaxing music and ask group members to recall both positive and negative experiences with their fathers. Allow the group ample time to remember several experiences. Periodically restate the instructions to keep the group focused. When the group appears to be finished their task, instruct them to slowly wake up and to quietly form a circle. Pass out paper and markers and ask the group to draw a picture of themselves and their fathers doing something. When the group has completed their drawings, ask each member to share their drawings with the group.

Write the word Father on the blackboard. Ask the group to brainstorm around all the things they enjoy doing with their fathers. When the list is completed, instruct the group to look over the list and select one or two activities they have not done with their fathers for a long time. Suggest that these may be activities to discuss with their father so they can do them again sometime.

Pass out paper and markers and ask the group members to complete the following statements.

**MY DAD**

1. One thing I like about my dad is ___________.
2. One thing I do not like about my dad is ___________.
3. I wish my dad would ___________.
4. It is a hard job being a father because ___________.
5. One way that I am the same as my dad is ___________.
6. When my dad gets angry he ___________.
7. When my dad feels happy he ___________.
8. One thing my dad does not know about is ___________.
9. I saw my dad sad when ___________.
10. My dad taught me to ___________.
11. One way I am different than my dad is ___________.
12. One more thing about my dad is ___________.

Share and discuss the completed statements. Complete the session with instructions for the group to recall all the lessons and strengths that each father has passed on to his child.

## Session IV: Healing the Loss

When children experience separation and divorce in their lives, they experience severe loss. These losses can have serious effects on later development. Children need to be encouraged to grieve the loss of what was, in order to be able to fully embrace that which is new and in many cases healthier.

Ask the group to recall the time their parents first decided to separate. How were they feeling? List all of the emotions and suggest those which may be over-looked. What were you saying to yourself in reference to the emotion? e.g., "I'm frightened because I think I will be alone more often now." Ask what they lost when their parents separated. Give suggestions and discuss.

Conduct a relaxation exercise in order to relieve some of the tension. Ask the children to allow themselves to feel some of these feelings of loss for five minutes only. Suggest to the group that they re-experience only these emotions that they can handle and only one emotion at a time. As the group is experiencing those painful moments, the group leader is to suggest that certain emotions can be represented by certain colors and certain shapes. The artist chooses the appropriate colors and shapes for an emotion. Instruct the group to create shapes and colors in their imagination that correspond to the different losses in their lives. When the group appears to have completed the task, ask them to slowly awaken themselves and to return to the circle. Reinforce feelings with the group that this remembering is a difficult and painful task. Explain that by expressing and understanding these situations, they may be able to put order into their thoughts and feelings and into their lives. Hand out large pieces of paper and a wide assortment of markers for the group. Ask the group members to draw the shapes and colors that they thought of during the relaxation exercise. When the task is completed, discuss the experience with the group and give each member ample time to express him/herself. Small groupings can ensure the members more time to talk. Ask group members to share their drawings with the whole group. When the task is completed, instruct the group to tighten the circle by moving closer. Request each member to make a quarter turn to the left. Each group member now has a back to massage. This exercise will help members to relieve physical tension. If the group still seems tense ask them to make a half turn and massage the back in front of them.

## Session V: Healing the Loss (continued)

Awareness and acknowledgment of the pain and a better appreciation of its effect on the self is a very useful and necessary step towards healing. The next step in the process is honouring what was and moving forward.

Ask group members to think back to painful experiences that were recalled in last session. Suggest to the group that they can remember some of these situations now without experiencing fear or pain. Explain that they can understand the situation a little better and that they can realize that they have survived; they are here today, getting healthier.

Ask the group to find a comfortable spot and use a simple relaxation exercise to quiet the group. Once they are relaxed, ask the group members to visualize a picture of themselves and how they looked when they were experiencing the pain of the family's breakup. Instruct them to be aware of the following: facial expression, body posture, type and colour of clothing, who else is with them, what is their environment like, are they saying anything to themselves, is anyone else speaking, if so, how does their voice sound, e.g., sad, angry, is there a kind of feeling or emotion in the room? When their past experience has been remembered, ask them to focus their attention on themselves. Suggest they get a good appreciation of their total experience of pain and loss. When the group appears to be finished, pass out paper and markers and ask them to draw a picture just of themselves and how they looked in their guided fantasy.

When their pictures are complete, ask the group to find a comfortable and quiet spot in the room and to focus their attention on their own drawings. Suggest to the group that they send loving and healing messages to the person in their pictures. Some messages might be "I love you." "You are a good boy/girl." "You have survived." "You are special." Ask them to reassure this character that they will always be there for them. When this is completed, ask them to silently ask the character in the picture what they need in order to feel safe again. Ask them to write down the words or messages they feel that the character in the drawing needs in order to be fully healed. Many children will write that they need their parents to reunite. Assure them that you understand this need and ask them to expand on what this reunion would give them. During the discussion ask them for alternative ways to get these necessary feelings, etc, that do not necessarily require Mom and Dad reuniting. Ask the group to take some time to fully realize what it is they need to feel whole again.

When the group has completed this phase of the session, ask them to form a circle and bring their drawings with them. Ask the group members one by one to explain their experience in the past and help each of them to appreciate that was how it was back then, and that they were powerless to change it. It just was. Now have each of them display their drawings and explain to the group what they feel they need now in order to fully heal themselves. Help each member to be specific about what their wants and needs are, how they can be met, and by whom.

When this phase is complete, ask the group members to go back to that comfortable and quiet place in the room where they were earlier. Instruct them to bring their drawings and their new awareness with them. When they appear to be settled and quiet, ask them to focus their attention on their drawings. Suggest that if they wish, they can communicate to the drawing as if it were them back then when they were experiencing the family breakup. Ask them to communicate in the best way they know, that their old selves can have their wants and needs met and that they have good ways to help them to heal.

Complete the session with some quiet play and then with a more active participant game in order to assist them in readjusting themselves to their next environment or activity.

## Session VI: Blended Families

Many children experience some form of new relationship development in their family constellation shortly after the separation. It might be with Mom's new boyfriend or Dad's new wife's children or Grandma moving in to help out; but, whatever the situation, it often causes more stress, more emotional upsets and further questions in the child or teen's already unstable state. There will be a few children in the group who have not experienced this; however, most of them have considered this possibility and in most cases, will experience this situation in their future.

Instruct the group to form a circle and to quietly relax themselves. Explain the concept of blended families and ask the group to suggest possible family compositions. Once the possibilities are exhausted, pass out the paper and markers and instruct group members to find a quiet and comfortable part of the room and to prepare themselves to draw. Ask the group members to draw their new family or families and to be sure to include all of the members that belong to each family grouping.

When this phase has been completed, ask the group to return to the circle and to present their new family or families to the group. For this part of the session it is useful for the group to merely state the characters' names and their relationship with the artist.

Once this has been completed, instruct the group to return to their quiet and comfortable spot with their drawing(s). Request that they place their drawings in front of them and that they focus their attention on the family. Ask "What problems does this family have?" "What do I dislike about each member?" "What problems might this family have in the future?" "How do I feel being in this family?" Instruct the group to write the answers to these questions somewhere on their drawing. It is useful to have the questions posted somewhere where the group can easily read them. Request that they go through this exercise with all of the families that they are involved with.

When this phase is completed, ask the group to return to the circle with their drawings. Give each child an opportunity to discuss their drawings with the group. Ask each member to present one drawing on the first turn and then another drawing each turn afterward until all have been discussed. While the child is presenting the problems within the family, ask the group to refrain from problem-solving for the child. They may ask questions for clarification of the problem but the problem-solving will come later.

When each member has presented his/her family and its problems, instruct the group to return to a quiet and comfortable space in the room and to bring their drawings with them. Instruct the group members to focus their attention on one of their drawings and ask, "What strengths or assets does this family have?" "What do I like about each member?" "How can I use the positive parts of this family to help me solve my problems within this family?" "How do I want to feel in this family?" "What needs to happen before I can feel this way in the family?" Instruct the group to write the answers to these questions somewhere on their drawings or on another piece of paper that they can attach to the drawing. Request that they go through this exercise with each of their drawings.

When this is completed, ask the group members to return to the circle again. Provide each child with the opportunity to discuss one of his/her drawings. This time the group can also provide feedback in terms of problem-solving to the artist if the child requests feedback. After each turn, encourage the child to write down any new awareness or solutions that come as a result of discussion with the group. Continue this process with the group until all of the members have presented all of their drawings.

Finally, ask the group members to return to their quiet and comfortable spaces once again. Instruct them to focus their attention on each drawing and to send positive messages to each member that they feel good about. They may send requests or demands silently to other members. When they feel finished with their first drawing, ask them to complete the process with any other drawings. Complete the session with an active game that requires group cooperation.

**Whether you think you can or you think you can't — you're right.**

**HENRY FORD**

## Bibliography for SPECIAL PROGRAMS

Clarke, J. (1978). *Self-esteem: A family affair.* Minneapolis, MN: Winston Press.

Duberman, L. (1975). *The reconstituted family.* Chicago: Nelson-Hall.

Ellis, A. (1984). *Rational-emotive therapy and cognitive behavior therapy.* New York: Springer.

Gordon, T. (1970 ). *Parent effectiveness training.* New York: Wyden.

Hendricks, G., & Roberts, T. (1977). *The second centering book.* Englewood Cliffs, NJ: Prentice-Hall.

Kelly, J., & Wallerstein, J. (1980). *Surviving the breakup.* New York: Basic Books.

Viscott, D. (1976). *The language of feelings.* New York: Pocket Books.

# CONCLUSION

**Games play no geographical bounds.**
**JACK BOTTERMANS**

The playing of games over the course of human history has managed to transcend social, political, linguistic, cultural, spiritual, environmental, and interpersonal barriers. The world has now reached a stage in its development where the power of play can be our strongest medicine in healing the planet and its inhabitants. The material in this text emphasizes the necessity of play in healthy childhood and teenage development. It highlights cooperative group activities and spontaneous creative group exercises as ways to make play time more beneficial and enjoyable. Within its pages lie countless strategies to improve the social climate and environment so that children and youth have the necessary play experiences to help them to develop into healthy adults, free of mind-body dysfunctions. When society frees itself of these dysfunctions, its members can then formulate solutions that will heal the wounded environment.

Childhood is a magicial time: it is a time when the human experience is unlimited in its capacity to live in the present. This living in the present allows the child to experience their vitality; when people in the child's world assist the child in cherishing this capacity, self-appreciation, self-love, and reverence for the other are easily attainable. Children who live in the present are participators in life; they feel confident that they have the ability to access their resources and those around them in order to solve life's challenges. They move with a boldness and see their world as being a wonderful place in which to live. A child who is forced to live in the past or the future becomes a spectator and more often a victim in life, feeling powerless because of past experiences and filled with anxiety about the future. When the child can be encouraged to experience life in the form of a game, an art activity, a role play, a team sport, spontaneous play experiences, or whatever is happening, the fears and anxieties of the past and the future disappear. The child and youth care professional's task is to make the activity interesting and attractive enough so that the child prefers to live in the present. The natural healing power of play and positive group interaction will heal the wounds of the past and lessen the anxieties of the future.

The text is an ever-present reminder that the professionals are responsible for their mind-body health and are required to model self-responsibility and self-love so as to motivate the child to continually strive for this goal. Self-reverence is an essential ingredient in life, for without this, the individual lives lost in a world that cannot be fulfilling. When the child and youth care professional can model and promote this self-responsible way of feeling and relating, children have a living example of their task in life. If children are unable to be filled with this sense of self-love by the significant adults in their life they are doomed to a life of trying to prove their worth. When they reach maturity they now must rely on themselves to generate this feeling of self-worth. This is extremely difficult to accomplish if the individual has limited experiences of this feeling of self-full-ness as opposed to a self-less-ness or a self-ish-ness. This reverence for the self is not a narcissistic love that excludes all others; nor,is it a self-less love that includes everyone else at the expense of the self. It is a sense of total commitment to the self and the self in the other; so, it includes the other in a state of mutual acceptance. The activities in this text can be used with this single purpose in mind and all other goals and purposes will automatically be accomplished.

Group interaction as a vehicle towards self-awareness, self-exploration, and self-responsibility represents the moving force behind this text. It is in relationship to the other that we appreciate ourselves and find meaning in our lives. This cannot be taught; it must be experienced. Group experiences provide the child with the opportunity to practise relationship development. Healthy facilitation with an emphasis on a healthy group environment increases the chances for the child to be successful. Hundreds of thousands of our children and youth long for this type of opportunity and with it, they can, no matter how difficult the past, learn to respond to love again, and to live life in a loving way.

Play has been the overall focus of this text and has been presented as the expression of the life-force, often called vitality. The models of play experiences for our modern-day children are ones that are highly competitive and at times they border on ruthlessness. The society has replaced the "play for play's sake" attitude with a "win at all costs" attitude. This rings true from the highly sophisticated sports programs to the excessive use of structured learning in the education systems. The playground has been replaced by the recreation room and the monkey bars by the joy sticks. Play times are relegated to fifteen minutes at recess and to the time it takes for the ride or walk home from school. Once home, television and computers take on the role of parents.

Play has been formalized to the mechanical and when the child acts in a spontaneous way, they are accused of cheating or not playing by the rules. The play toys of the past decades lack imagination and are picture perfect in every detail. No longer does the branch of a tree double as the king's sceptor and the knight's sword. Today, each child has an authentic replica of the M-1 machine gun, one that makes the real sound. Time for spontaneous play is being used up by homework, excessive television, and an over- involvement in formalized athletics. The expectations of parents and other adults in the child's life stress a race towards maturity. "Grow up!" "Act your age!" "Speak when you are spoken to." Children and youth are being asked to act with adult maturity without being given the time to reach that level of maturity.

Child and youth care professionals can challenge these unimaginative and stifling forms of play by introducing creative and challenging activities and spontaneous play experiences. This type of programming will allow children to experience life in their own bodies and to express this experience through their emotions. Children are naturally adept at experiencing life in this way. All they need is the opportunity to do so.

My greatest wish, as I complete this text, is that it will be used and expanded upon by the professionals who work with the earth's most precious resource: the children and youth of today.

**The earth is not ours to own; it is on loan to us by our children.**

**ANONYMOUS**

## THE AUTHOR

Michael Burns has been working as a front-line child and youth care professional for the past twenty years. His experiences as a program coordinator, a program developer, an educator, and a therapist have contributed to a unique text that embodies the practice of child and youth care. Michael received his diploma in Child and Youth Care from St. Clair Community College in Windsor, Ontario; he obtained his degree in Sociology at the University of Windsor; and he is completing his Master's Degree in Education at St. Francis Xavier University in Antigonish, Nova Scotia.

This is Michael's second book in the area of child and youth care; his first book, *Stories in Child Care: A Metaphorical Approach to Change*, was a compilation of fifteen therapeutic metaphors to be used with children and youth. This book has been used by several colleges and universities in both Canada and the United States.

Michael operates a private practice with his partner, Sandra Johnston, in Sarnia, Ontario, where they both function as therapists, consultants, and trainers in a wide variety of areas in the mental health field. He is the father of two children and was born into a family of eight children. Michael has spent his life working and playing in child and youth groups.

Michael is working on his third book in the area of child and youth care. This book focuses on the roles necessary for effective parenting. He suggests to parents that although the nuturing role of parenting is an innate quality, they will need to fully develop this quality in order to parent effectively. The role of educator and behavior manager are not roles that parents are born with, but are skills that must be learned and developed if parents expect to be sucessful in raising healthy, self-reliant children of the twenty-first century.

The Journal of Child and Youth Care

presents

# TIME IN

## A Handbook for Child and Youth Care Professionals

## by Michael Burns

"Practitioners have been waiting for this solid, good-natured, practical book for a long time, and here it is!"

Jerome Beker, Ph.D.
Editor, *Child and Youth Care Forum*

"Highly recommended for all people willing to engage in recreation at a challenging new level."

Jack Phelan, M.A.Psyc.
Grant MacEwan College

"What an antidote this rich compendium of various games, exercises, and ideas can be to the dreary, boring, and rigid environments governed by a control theme and behavior modification programs."

Karen VanderVen, Ph.D.
University of Pittsburgh

**Time In** makes an excellent gift for any individual who works with children, youth, or adults in groups. Specifically, it will interest teachers, day care workers, psychologists, social workers, youth group leaders, parents, and, indeed, anyone who is still a child at heart.